ELECTRONICS AFLOAT

ELECTRONICS AFLOAT

Dag Pike

NAUTICAL

© Dag Pike 1986

First published in Great Britain by
Nautical Books
an imprint of
Conway Maritime Press Ltd
24 Bride Lane
Fleet Street
London EC4Y 8DR

ISBN 0 85177 390 7

Typeset and designed by Trevor Ridley Creative Services, Southend-on-Sea
Printed by Alden Press, Oxford

Contents

	Introduction	**6**
1	Decca, Loran and others	**9**
2	Satellites in the sky	**22**
3	Radar to see	**33**
4	The old faithful — Radio Direction Finding	**45**
5	The lead and the log, also compasses, and autopilots	**55**
6	Wind and weather displayed	**70**
7	Chart by electronics	**76**
8	When chip speaks to chip	**83**
9	Navigation	**91**
10	Racing	**107**
11	Hear and speak	**113**
12	Safety, security and even television	**129**
13	Installation and power supplies	**135**
	Index	**143**

INTRODUCTION

The use of electronics on yachts has increased dramatically in recent years. It was inevitable that miniaturisation and the ability to package powerful equipment in compact cases to enable it to stand up to rough treatment would have lead to this increasing use, but ironic when one realises that the sea is probably the harshest environment for electronic equipment. Behind the growth in yacht electronics is the development of the micro computer.

The micro computer processes complex information in micro-seconds and today the development of yacht electronics is not limited by the capabilities of the equipment, but by what the yachtsman will be prepared to accept and pay for. We have reached a stage where almost everything is possible with yacht electronics and this can make it hard for the yachtsman to decide what to purchase and how to use the equipment.

One of the main functions of this book is to evaluate current and future electronic systems for yachts, and show their applications and their limitations so as to ensure that the yachtsman can make the right choice of equipment and use it intelligently.

There is almost unlimited potential in modern electronics. Position finding systems which will tell you where you are with a high degree of accuracy anywhere in the world, are under development. Integrated electronic systems can tell you how to keep your yacht sailing at maximum efficiency whether you are using wind or engine propulsion. Radar lets you see in the dark and in fog, whilst electronic charts and plotters will soon combine many of these elements to take navigation away from the chart table and on to the screen.

At present all of these systems have limitations which make them less than perfect and so the challenge remains. The navigator must be aware of these limitations, must plan within them, and still exercise skill if he is to sail in safety. However, it is very easy to be lulled into a false sense of security, to accept what the instrument says at face value and to follow the electronic course blindly. This is where we have to look carefully at the way in which information is displayed. In many instruments on the market today, the information is shown in a very precise form — so precise that it takes a brave person to dispute the figures. Yet every electronic instrument has errors of one sort or another and these must be taken into the reckoning for safe navigation.

The choice of display is important. Ideally, the display should give some idea of the accuracy of the information being shown, but no manufacturer wants to admit that an instrument is not accurate, and in most cases, the yachtsman is left to make his own judgement. Graphic displays are developing rapidly and the flexibility offered by this type of presentation follows the increasing use of graphics for computer displays in general. They allow complex information generated by integrated electronics to be displayed in a readily understandable form.

Control knobs or key pads can make or break a system and development continues. You may be able to operate equipment easily and comfortably in the showroom, but consider the situation on board. Fingers may be cold and wet, the yacht may be tossing around and it can be very difficult to operate a small keyboard accurately. The keying operations should be as simple as possible and the design of the keyboard should take into account the conditions under which it will be used especially as electronics become miniaturised. There is no point in having small equipment if you cannot control it efficiently on board.

At the present level of use, any equipment failure is not too alarming, you can always resort to traditional dead reckoning navigation. However, with increasing reliance on electronics, these traditional skills may gradually be lost.

The solution lies in providing redundancy in the electronic systems so that failure will never be total. As the cost of electronic equipment continues to fall in real terms it becomes more practical to think in terms of adding a back-up system in the essential areas such as position finding.

Damp is the worst enemy of electronics, closely followed by vibration. That electronics can operate reliably under these conditions is a tribute to the design and development of yacht electronics. The degree of protection against damp and vibration built into a piece of equipment is usually reflected in the price, and the yachtsman should consider this when deciding where and how the equipment will be used.

Open cockpit mounting in a yacht demands full waterproofing. There can be no compromise on this if the equipment is to stand a chance of working satisfactorily. Some manufacturers pretend that splashproof equipment will do the job but, on a yacht, water comes from all directions, often with considerable force and only fully waterproof equipment can withstand the onslaught.

You may want to see instruments from the cockpit, but they can be mounted behind a windscreen or in the companionway. Splashproof equipment may well survive this sort of exposure, but any equipment not coming in the waterproof or splashproof category should be consigned to the chart table or to a fully enclosed wheelhouse. Even here, damp can be a problem when you come in from outside with dripping oilskins. It doesn't take much water to cause havoc with electronic systems.

Keeping the water out is therefore essential. Reliable power supplies are equally important. Yacht systems have tended to suffer from poor or casual installation techniques which failed to recognise the demanding conditions under which they were expected to operate. Most yacht builders today recognise the importance of reliable electrical systems on yachts, both for comfort and safety, but if the advantages of modern electronics are to be fully realised then power supplies must match up to electronic reliability.

The use of electronics is increasing rapidly and from a full monitoring role it is a short step to complete automation. This may not be a path which every yachtsman will want to follow. Whether you decide to hang on to your RDF or go the whole way to satellite navigation and communication, a better understanding of how the various systems operate and what they will do, will allow you to decide the role that electronics will fulfil for you.

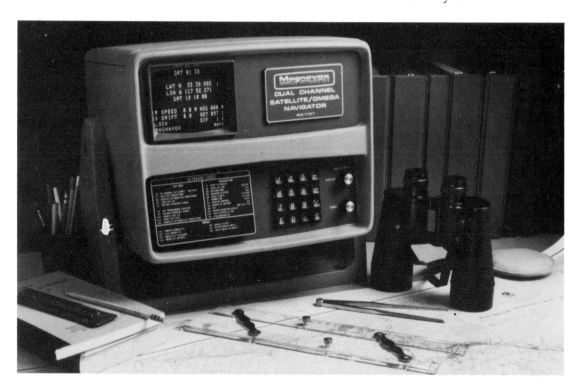

A combined satnav and Omega receiver. These two units exchange information which helps to upgrade the accuracy of the positions from both systems.

1 Decca, Loran and others

Hyperbolic navigation systems get their name from the shape of the position lines they generate. The position line is found by measuring the time or phase difference between signals sent from two transmitting stations and the line of equal time or phase is hyperbolic in shape when shown on the chart. A similar position line generated from a second pair of transmitters enables the observer's position to be determind at the point where the two position lines cross.

The principle is quite simple, but in practice there are a number of factors which have to be taken into account in arriving at a reasonably accurate position. The transmitted signals are affected in a number of ways which can degrade the accuracy. Modern micro-processors have, however, enabled these hyperbolic systems to be developed into compact receivers which give continuous position finding information with a very useful degree of accuracy.

There are four different types of hyperbolic position finding systems in operation. Only Omega offers worldwide coverage, whilst the others offer a more localised coverage, but with a higher degree of accuracy. Omega's worldwide cover is achieved at the expense of accuracy whilst the alternative systems, Loran C, Decca Navigator and Toran generally give their best accuracy close to land where it is most needed. Accuracy degrades out to sea. Loran C offers a longer range capability than the other two systems, but Decca Navigator and Toran can give higher accuracies in the coastal regions they cover.

The hyperbolic position lines generated by these position finding systems demanded the use of special charts when the systems were first introduced. These charts were overprinted with a lattice of position lines by means of which the navigator could plot his position. Modern electronics now enable the position line position to be translated into a latitude and longitude position so that special charts are no longer needed. However, this translation of the position into latitude and longitude does degrade the accuracy to a certain extent and it can also make it difficult to apply the various corrections necessary to obtain high accuracy.

Latitude and longitude readouts from these position finding systems seem to provide everything the navigator needs, but they must be treated with a degree of caution. The very positive nature of the display gives no hint of the degree of accuracy and whilst the accuracy will generally be adequate for coastal navigation, the positions must be used with caution if you are making a landfall in fog or trying to navigate to close tolerances. Because the errors and corrections are different for each system they will be dealt with individually.

Decca Navigator

Decca Navigator was a product of World War II and it has been steadily refined and developed ever since. Its use for yachts is comparatively recent because the system is privately operated and the receivers were only available on rental at a fairly high annual charge, making them uneconomic for yacht use. The receivers are now compact, simple to operate and can be bought over the counter which has widened the market considerably.

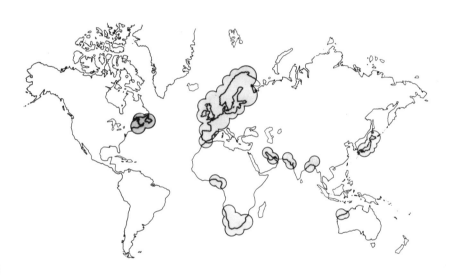

Coverage of the Decca Navigator system worldwide. The Canadian east coast system is being closed down.

The Decca Navigator system is operated by Racal-Decca, generally as a private venture, but with government support in some countries. The system operates as a series of chains; each chain comprising a master transmitter and three slaves. Coverage extends over the whole of Northern Europe and down to Gibraltar and into the Western Mediterranean, the coasts of South Africa, the Arabian Gulf, Nigeria, parts of India and most of the waters around Japan. For yachtsmen the coverage is usually extensive enough to cover prolonged cruising in the areas which are covered and the chains have, in general, been planned to ensure that the accuracy is good in areas where navigation may be tricky.

The Decca Navigator system provides a position line by

measuring the phase difference between signals transmitted from a master and a slave station. These signals are phase locked so that when the peak of a wave is transmitted from the master transmitter, a similar peak is transmitted from the slave. When the receiver picks up these signals it is able to determine the phase difference between them. This indicates that the vessel is on a particular position line. Two position lines from two different master/slave combinations give a fix, which will then be converted into a latitude and longitude.

The accuracy of the Decca Navigator system is best when closest to the transmitting stations, although there can be large errors when very close to a transmitter, particularly when on the base line extension — the extension of a line joining two transmitters. The accuracy decreases with distance from the transmitters; the effective range being in the order of 300-400 miles by day and 200-300 miles at night. With yacht receivers which switch from one chain to another automatically, the user may not be aware of where the transmitters are in relation to the yacht's position, but this can have a considerable influence on the accuracy obtained from the system. Because of this, a chart of the transmitters should be carried on board.

Close to the transmitters, the accuracy can be better than 50 metres, but at 300 miles it may only be ½ mile. There are tables of fixed errors available, but these only relate to position lines and not to latitude and longitude so they are difficult to apply.

Distortion can occur when the signals from the transmitters to the yacht pass over land, and the accuracy of the Decca Navigator system can deteriorate in enclosed or semi-enclosed waters. The system relies on the transmitted signals taking the direct path from the transmitter to the yacht's antenna, following the earth's surface. The signal can, however, also reach the yacht via the longer sky wave path where it is reflected on the ionosphere. The sky wave signals can interfere with the direct signal causing an error which will vary with the time of day and the season of the year. Corrections are available that upgrade the accuracy for these variable errors. These can be from 100 metres to 2 miles. But particularly where larger errors are concerned, the position should be used with caution.

Despite these possible errors in the accuracy of the system, the modern Decca Navigator receiver is a useful navigation tool. It offers continuous position finding with very little effort on the part of the navigator. It is effective in fog and rain when visibility is reduced and provided that reasonable caution is exercised about the accuracy, such as checking the position against the readings of the echo sounder, can be used with considerable confidence.

In order that that receiver can lock on to the correct phase of the transmitted signals, the position of the yacht to within 10 miles or so has to be known when the receiver is first switched on. This presents little problem in port, but could be a problem when sailing into Decca coverage from seaward. It could also be a problem if there was an interruption in the power supplies.

Some modern receivers give an indication of the reliability of the received signals and this in turn gives an indication of how much the indicated position can be trusted. These indicators, which usually take the form of different coloured lights, are only a guide, but in the absence of any other means of confirmation they can help. Most receivers will operate happily at speeds up to 25 knots, but if you have a fast motor boat, then you may have to select one of the receivers which can operate at higher speeds. Single channel receivers only process the signal from one master/slave combination at a time whilst multi-channel receivers give simultaneous processing which can cope with higher speeds.

All Decca Navigator receivers available for yacht use incorporate the facility for waypoint navigation. Many other features, such as indicators showing the chain being used and testing facilities to show that the receiver is functioning correctly are also incorporated. As many as 30 different types of data can be displayed but in practice only a few of these are used for most navigations tasks. The Decca Navigator system has a high level of repeatable accuracy and we will show how this can be exploited to improve the level of navigation accuracy.

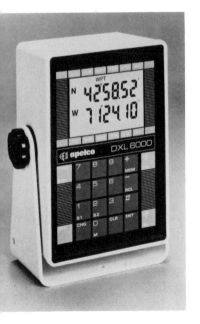

The latest style of Loran C receiver with vertical format which takes up less space. The large LCD display is a feature of modern receivers.

Loran C.

The Decca Navigator system is very similar to Loran C, but there are also critical differences which need to be understood to obtain the best from the system. Loran C operates by measuring both time and phase differences between the received signals and this enables it to make use of the sky wave component thus increasing the range of coverage. Loran C also operates at a lower frequency and whilst this helps to increase the range of coverage, it can also increase interference from other signals.

Loran C uses the same format of master and slave stations as Decca Navigator but, because of the increased range of the system, these are placed further apart than with Decca Navigator. Some of the chains only have two slaves, but three is the norm. The coverage of Loran C is extensive and embraces the whole coastline of the USA including the southern coasts of Alaska. There is also coverage in Japanese waters and over many areas of the Pacific Ocean. Coverage extends over most of the northern parts of the Atlantic Ocean and parts of Northern Europe and the Mediterranean. Loran C coverage extends a considerable distance offshore and it is a viable ocean navigation system in some regions although the coverage is too intermittent for general use in ocean navigation.

Worldwide coverage of the Loran C system. The shaded areas show the approximate ground wave coverage.

The Loran C system works on the principle that radio waves travel at a constant speed. When master and slave stations transmit a pulse at the same time, the time difference (TD) between the arrival of the two signals establishes the position of the receiver along a position line. This hyperbolic position line is matched by a similar position line from another master/slave combination. The receiver is at the position where the two lines cross.

Loran C transmitters send out a signal comprising a series of pulses and these are analysed and matched in the receiver when measuring the time difference between their receipt. The signal from the master station has a ninth pulse built in so that it can be recognised. Because the matching of the signals is carried out by a phase comparison method, higher accuracies are possible than with the original Loran A system which carried out a much more basic time comparison. This phase comparison helps to eliminate sky wave problems. At longer ranges the sky wave can be used for position fixing, but with greatly reduced accuracy.

Because the Loran C system is based on time, very high accuracy clocks are required at the transmission station. The on-board receiver is only, however, measuring the time difference and not absolute time so that these expensive clocks are not required in the receiver.

A Loran C receiver with a remote reading off-course and distance-to-go dial. This dial can be mounted at an exterior steering position and gives the helmsman sufficient information for course corrections to reach a given waypoint.

Most Loran C receivers display the position as a latitude and longitude although the time differences are also available for those using the special overprinted charts. Corrections have to be applied to both types of position to improve accuracy and unlike the Decca Navigation system, a table of latitude and longitude corrections has been produced by the US Defence Mapping Agency. These corrections are largest where the signal has passed over land and to apply them it is necessary to know the particular master and slave stations in use. This can be found by using one of the alternative displays on the receiver. In most cases the user has to select the required stations anyway and to find the optimum group for a particular area, a chart of the various chains is required. Ideally this should also show the position line pattern so that the crossing gradients, and hence the accuracy for a particular area, can be established. The area around the base line extension should not be used for position fixing because of very poor accuracy.

On some receivers it is possible for the corrections to be applied electronically so that the display shows the corrected positions but this only applies to the fixed errors. Variable errors have to be applied by the navigator. In areas of enclosed water such as ports and harbours the land effect can be considerable and Loran C should not be used. In general this system should only be used where the fixed corrections have been catalogued.

All Loran C transmissions are around the 100kHz frequency. The transmissions within a particular group or chain are spaced so that they do not interfere with each other. Adjacent groups have a different Group Repetition Interval to eliminate interference from adjacent transmitters. The 100kHz frequency, however, is susceptible to interference from a number of outside sources. It is the level of the interference and the strength of the received signal which effectively determines the range at which the receiver can provide reliable positions.

Electrical noise, both from on-board sources and from external sources is one of the main culprits in reducing the sensitivity of a Loran C receiver. The problem becomes more acute as the frequency of the interference approaches 100kHz or multiples of this figure. On-board television receivers can generate low powered transmissions which can cause a problem and high power, low frequency transmitters on shore can also generate interference.

There are of course ways to cope with interference in order to get the best Loran C signal. One is to eliminate the interference and this can only be done with that generated on board. A good quality receiver is fitted with some form of noise-to-signal level meter and by switching off each piece of on-board equipment in sequence, it will soon become apparent, which is the culprit. Fluorescent

A Loran C receiver with a large number of dedicated control buttons which, although looking more complex, helps to simplify the operation of the receiver.

lighting and engine ignition systems are common causes of interference.

Interference which cannot be eliminated can be reduced by the use of notch filters. On some receivers, these filters are internally controlled and need special test equipment. This is usually the case when a noise to signal level meter is not fitted. The adjustment should always be made by an experienced technician. Where externally adjustable notch filters are fitted these can be adjusted by the operator to improve the signal clarity, but great care must be taken not to reduce the Loran C signal in attempts to cut back the interference.

A combination of these two methods should produce an acceptable level of signal reception, but it must be recognised that the signal level will deteriorate with distance from the transmitters. This will make the positions obtained less reliable. At the same time the accuracy deteriorates with distance from the transmitters because a 0.1 microsecond time difference between the signals corresponds to a greater distance on the ground.

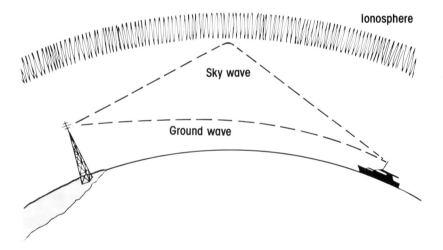

Ionosphere

Sky wave

Ground wave

The longer route taken by Skywave, Loran C signals which can create inaccuracies. Positions over 1000 miles from a transmitter may be suspect.

Fortunately, in most cases this reduction in accuracy tends to be in areas where accuracy is less important.

The accuracy of Loran C is stated by the US Coast Guard, who operate the system, to be between 0.1 and 0.25 nautical miles within the areas designated for coverage. These are probably cautious figures and much better accuracy should be obtainable in areas of good coverage. They do, however, represent a good guide to the level of accuracy to expect when navigating in fog, but remember to apply the necessary corrections to obtain this level of accuracy. These figures would apply up to 300-400 miles from the transmitters but at greater ranges the accuracy could deteriorate down to 1 mile or worse as the sky wave effect comes into play.

When the cycle alarm light or the signal-to-noise ratio is low, any position should be treated with caution.

A wide range of receivers are available for use on board yachts and price is a good indication of quality and features. However, a company with a high volume of production should be able to produce quality at a lower price and a recently developed receiver may use new low-cost techniques, so that features are the only real guide to quality. The areas where cheap receivers may cut back are in the notch filters, automatic correction for fixed errors, number of waypoints available and the type of display. The display should have at least two lines so that both latitude and longitude can be shown at the same time. The size of a receiver can give a guide to how recently it was developed, although the limit of size compatible with easy use on board a yacht may have already been reached. Loran C has a high repeatable accuracy, like Decca Navigator, and this virtue can be exploited with suitable navigation techniques. It offers a good general-purpose navigation system, but like all these hyperbolic navigation systems, it must be used with a degree of caution.

Omega

The original concept for the Omega system was developed by Decca and it is a similar phase-synchronised system. Because it operates on very low frequencies, between 10.2 and 13.6kHz it has

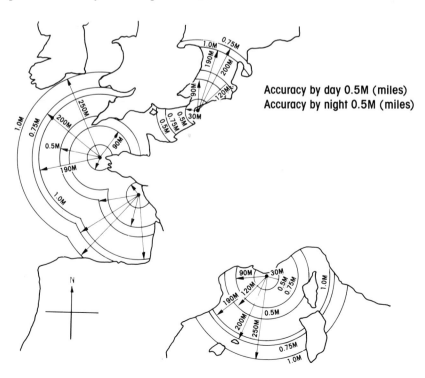

The accuracy limits of the French differential Omega systems showing considerable variations between day and night accuracy.

Accuracy by day 0.5M (miles)
Accuracy by night 0.5M (miles)

a much longer range than the Decca Navigator system, but there is a consequent reduction in accuracy. Omega is operated on an international basis with eight transmitters located around the world.

These transmitters operate on four common frequencies and one unique-station frequency. With a suitable receiver, the signals from any two suitable stations can generate a position line through phase comparison and two position lines will give a position. The stated accuracy of Omega is 4 nautical miles with a 95 per cent confidence, but in practice accuracy levels of around 2 nautical miles can be expected in many areas.

The main factor affecting accuracy is the signal propogation variation and this is being assessed in various regions of the world in order to produce a valid table of corrections. Corrections can be applied manually or automatically.

In order to maintain the lane count necessary to give accurate positions, the Omega receiver has to be initialised at a known position. From here the lane count is maintained automatically, but any interruption may make it difficult to get in sequence again unless the position is known with reasonable accuracy.

Two types of receiver are available — single and multi-channel, the former being adequate for yacht use. Omega receivers have a limited market and for yachts the system is only really applicable to those undertaking ocean passages. The market is very limited and no receivers have been developed specifically for yacht use.

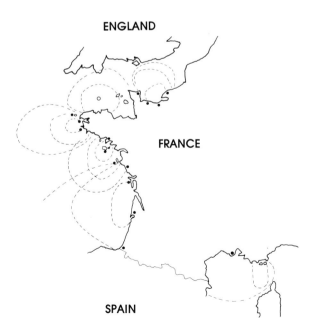

ENGLAND

FRANCE

SPAIN

Coverage of the French Toran system with the lines showing 2, 5 and 10 metre accuracy levels.

RANA and Toran

RANA is a position finding system developed in France. It is similar in many respects to Loran C but operates on higher frequencies between 300 and 400 kHz. This gives the system very high accuracy levels but limits the effective range. RANA transmitters provide position finding coverage over all the French Atlantic coastline extending out to 400 miles by day and 200 miles by night. The accuracy level is 10 metres over most of the coastal region diminishing to 200 metres further offshore.

Toran is a phase comparison system similar to Decca Navigator but works on much higher frequencies on the 2MHz band. This limits the range, but gives very high accuracy and two chains using this system are operational in the English Channel region where rannge is less important than accuracy. Both Toran and RANA are operated by the French Lighthouse Authority, and the more accurate Toran is being expanded to cover the Bay of Biscay.

Receivers

Modern receivers operating on all of these hyperbolic position finding systems do much more than just indicate the position. Most of the receivers now on the market and aimed specifically at the yacht market are fully-fledged navigation computers which produce most of the information required to navigate a yacht safely.

There are many variations from receiver to receiver but the main secondary function is to enable waypoint navigation to be carried out. Waypoint navigation involves determining the various positions you want your course to pass through and then feeding the latitude and longitude of these positions into the receiver. The receiver then calculates the course and distance between these points, but of more immediate value it indicates the course to steer and the distance to go to the next waypoint. It will also indicate the distance you are one side or the other of the pre-determined track, so that at a glance you are aware of the navigation status of your yacht. This is much easier than laboriously plotting each latitude and longitude position on the chart.

The receiver will also calculate speed and course made good over the ground which can be very valuable information. Indeed there is almost a surfeit of information available so that in practice you tend to limit its use to two or three of the more valuable functions. However the information can be given to other instruments with the most common being a link with the autopilot which will then maintain the yacht on course automatically if you instruct it accordingly.

A receiver's ability to handle a large number of waypoints can be useful. Although you may only use a few on any one passage, these can be stored in the memory and called up for use when required. This saves taking the positions off the chart each time and speeds up voyage planning.

Modern position finding receivers are very compact and comparatively cheap. There tends to be a direct connection between quality and price, but with rapid developments taking place in electronic technology a cheaper receiver may achieve a lower price through advanced technology. Points to look for in selecting a receiver are low power consumption, good memory capability when the receiver is switched off, large waypoint capability, simple installation, good filter system (Loran C receivers), ease of use and understandable handbook. Water-proofing can be a useful feature if the receiver is installed in an exposed position. The type of control keys should also be considered and those with a tactile feel are best as they give a positive indication that the key has made contact.

For the smaller yacht, the best receivers are those with single key strokes for the important functions. You do not want to be messing with the keys when the yacht is bouncing around. One of the attractions of these receivers is the ability to plan the passage before you sail and pre-programme the receiver. Then if the going gets tough offshore, the navigation requirement is greatly simplified. One of the advantages of having a large waypoint memory is that even if you change your plans it is quite simple to call up a new waypoint.

Antenna Requirements

Technology has greatly enhanced antennae for these position finding receivers. The length of antenna is generally a function of the mean frequency it is designed to handle and for the low frequency systems such as Loran C and Omega, a very long antenna would be best. However, a much shorter whip antenna can be used in conjunction with a pre-amplifier to give adequate results.

All of the systems mentioned in this chapter are subject to interference from outside sources and to get the best results the antenna should be mounted as high and as far from other antennae stays, masts and other metal objects as possible. On sailing yachts the top of the mast is a logical location, but here the VHF antenna might have priority. If there is a choice between an elevated location and a clear location, then the clear location should be the one chosen, to allow the maximum signal to get to the receiver with the least possible interference.

Both the antenna casing and the receiver itself need to be very carefully earthed. This can make a tremendous difference to the interference levels and consequently the quality of the positions. It is better to prevent interference from reaching the receiver rather than trying to cancel it out with the filter. Whilst less sensitive to interference, the antennae for Decca Navigator and Toran still require careful siting and should be accorded due priority if the best results are to be obtained.

Differential Systems and Repeatability

Differential navigation systems are a very simple way of increasing the accuracy of hyperbolic systems. In their simplest form differential techniques can be used to check the system every time a yacht leaves harbour, but more complex differential systems are used to upgrade the accuracy of a system in selected areas.

Differential systems are currently in use for both Loran C and Omega. In essence, they comprise a shore-bound receiver, the position of which is accurately known. The position determined by this receiver can then be compared with the actual position and this produces a series of corrections which can be applied to other receivers in the vicinity in order to upgrade their accuracy. The corrections are transmitted over a dedicated radio link and can be applied automatically.

Differential systems working in connection with Loran C receivers are operating in some US harbours. This gives the system sufficient accuracy for harbour use and helps to overcome the problems caused by the signal passing overland in enclosed waters. Accuracies of 5-10 yards can be obtained in this way and the corrections could be valid for beteen 20 and 50 miles from the tracking station. A system operating on Omega has been developed by the French authorities to cover the Western Approaches and the French coast and accuracies of ¼-½ mile are claimed.

These differential systems may be expanded, but will have only limited application to yachts because of the anticipated cost. A yacht can, however, develop its own system which, whilst it may not give quite the same degree of accuracy, will at least give greater confidence in the system. The yacht need only be close to a fixed object so that the actual and true readings can be compared. Taking the fixed point as the true reading, it is then a simple matter to work out latitude and longitude corrections to apply.

If accuracy is required in harbour then the fixed point should be in the harbour, but clear of wharves, buildings, shipping etc. If for use at sea then an open water lighthouse or beacon should be used. Floating objects such as buoys are not really suitable because they move around.

Another way of using hyperbolic systems is to exploit their repeat accuracy. If you take a set of readings, you can later return very close to the same position, particularly if it is a similar time of day. Take readings on important fairway or other buoys in clear weather and you can be fairly sure of finding them again in fog. This is a form of differential navigation because such a technique at least rules out the fixed errors, if not the variable ones.

Future Developments

The introduction of the Navstar GPS satellite position finding system threatens the future existence of all of these hyperbolic systems. It offers a comparable degree of accuracy and worldwide coverage. US funding for overseas Loran C chains is to be withdrawn in the early 1990's. This would mean that the Loran chains covering the Mediterranean, Northern Europe and Japan would go although there have been some moves by other governments to retain these chains and even extend them to provide a secondary or back-up position finding system.

Discussions are likely to take place with the partner nations involved in Omega with a view to winding up this service once Navstar GPS becomes operational. The US coverage of Loran C is also under threat of shut-down in due course, but this is not likely to be before the year 2000. Decca Navigator, being a commercially operated system, is likely to continue whilst it is still viable and even then may get government support to be continued as a secondary or independent system to Navstar GPS. Toran will probably follow the same path.

A great deal of time change is dependent on the rate at which users switch to Navstar GPS. Because yachtsmen represent by far the largest group of potential users in the marine world, they will have considerable influence, and yachtsmen are likely to make a fairly rapid switch to the new system because of its simplicity, accuracy, wide coverage and lack or errors. Thus hyperbolic systems would appear to have a finite life but one which is not likely to terminate before the year 2000.

The first of the low cost satnav receivers. The limitations of this receiver can be seen in the single line display which doesn't allow a full position to be shown at one time.

2 Satellites in the sky

The concept of yachts navigating through direct contact with satellites would have sounded very far fetched a few years ago, but today it is a reality and tomorrow new developments promise high-accuracy, worldwide systems which will probably make all other navigation systems obsolete. Satellite navigation for yachts reflects the remarkable capabilities of the modern micro-computer around which the yacht receivers are based.

The current satellite navigation system in operation is Transit which has a history stretching back over 20 years. The first marine receiver operating on Transit was used in 1963 and the system is based on a very simple concept. When the first satellites put into orbit in the late 1950s it was found that their orbits could be plotted by taking Doppler measurements of the transmitted radio signal at

The components of the Transit satellite navigation system.

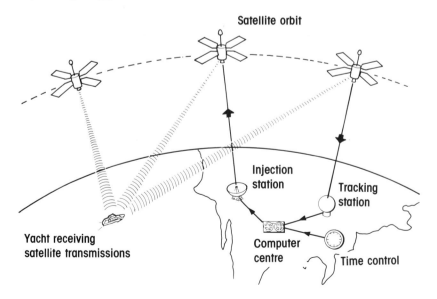

Satellite orbit

Injection station

Tracking station

Yacht receiving satellite transmissions

Computer centre

Time control

intervals when the satellite was above the horizon of a receiving station in a known position. If the satellite could be accurately plotted this way, it was reasoned that the system could be used in reverse to determine the position of a receiver on the ground.

Development was pursued by the US Navy to create a position fixing system for the Polaris submarines. By 1963 the Transit system was operational with five satellites in orbit and in 1967 the system was made available for commercial development. The necessary computers for processing the satellite information were still large and power-hungry at this time and development of receivers was concentrated on the commercial shipping market. In 1977 there were only around 2000 commercial receivers in use, but by 1980 the compact micro-processor had made its appearance and growth became dramatic.

The compact micro-processor allowed receivers to be made small enough and cheap enough for the yacht market. This in turn provided the high volume market which further reduced the price and today Transit satellite receivers are widely used on yachts despite their limitation of intermittent position fixing.

The support system for Transit is complex despite the apparent simplicity of the basic concept. The satellites are in polar orbits 1075 kilometres high, circling the earth every 107 minutes. These form a 'birdcage' net around the earth and a satellite is available for a position fix every 35 to 100 minutes, depending on the observer's latitude: the higher the latitude, the shorter the interval.

Three tracking stations monitor the progress of the satellites and receive the transmitted signals. The Doppler data on these signals is transmitted to the control centre in California where the satellite orbits are precisely determined. Each time a satellite passes over a tracking station updated information about its precise orbit is passed to the satellite, and this information is in turn transmitted to earth in the signal which is picked up by the yacht receiver.

Because only one satellite is used to determine the yacht's position, two readings from the satellite are necessary to determine position. The satellite transmits a navigation message every two minutes giving details of its orbit, and Doppler measurements from this signal are used to determine the yacht's position. The whole process of obtaining a position may take from 10 to 16 minutes as the satellite crosses the sky, but this allows a long baseline to improve the accuracy.

Because of the time involved, the yacht's motion across the earth's surface has to be taken into account in the calculations and this is why a course and speed input is required for Transit receivers. This can be inserted manually through the keyboard, but most receivers will accept automatic log and compass inputs to automate the process.

A fully fledged satnav receiver with a multi-line display which allows most commonly used navigation information to be shown in one display page.

A combined satnav and Loran C receiver which can upgrade the position accuracy in areas towards the limits of Loran coverage.

Transit is a worldwide position finding system and for many years it was the only system which could claim this distinction. Omega is now challenging this role, but with a lower level of accuracy. Against this must be weighed the intermittent nature of the Transit fixes compared with the continuous coverage of Omega.

However very few yachtsmen are interested in worldwide coverage and are generally only interested in position finding within, at most, a few hundred miles from their home port. Systems such as Loran C and Decca Navigator can generally provide adequate accuracy over limited ranges where there is coverage, but Transit can still be an attractive system even in these areas because it offers a high degree of reliability and is virtually free from interference and distortion. It is not affected by weather conditions like the land-based systems.

If a Transit receiver is used from a stationary yacht then the accuracy levels will be good, possibly within 50 metres or so. Once the yacht is moving the errors tend to increase, largely because the yacht's speed and compass inputs are rarely accurate enough to maintain high levels of position finding accuracy. It is speed and course over the ground which the Transit receiver needs so that even with log and compass inputs allowance still has to be made for the effects of current, tide and leeway.

The position errors which can be generated by incorrect speed inputs can be quite considerable. Given a good satellite pass, a one knot error in the speed in a north — south direction could lead to a position error of about ¼ mile, with the maximum error being in the longitude. With a bad satellite pass, when the satellite is nearly overhead, this error could grow to nearly one mile.

These errors can sound quite alarming, and whilst errors in the speed input can occur, all is not lost. Some Transit receivers are self-compensating to a degree. Between satellite fixes, the Transit receiver operates in the dead-reckoning mode, using the course and speed inputs as well as any manually inserted current, tide or leeway inputs, to update the displayed position continuously. When the next satellite fix is made, this fix is compared with the current DR position and the difference, deemed to be set and drift, is added into the DR calculations to upgrade the accuracy.

Because of its inherently high level of accuracy and the fact that it is unaffected by atmospheric conditions, Transit receivers are often combined with a Loran C or Omega receiver. These secondary receivers have a high level of repeatability so they can provide an accurate speed and course input which, when used in conjunction with the satellite fixes, gives a good level of accuracy both at the time of the fix and at the intervals in between. This combination also provides a back-up in the event of failure of one

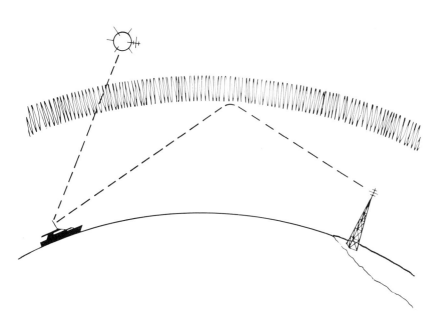

By integrating Loran C with satnav, position accuracy can be upgraded particularly in areas of skywave Loran C coverage.

or other of the systems and represents a good compromise.

During the interval between satellite fixes, the DR positions are adequate for most yacht navigation even when the receiver is used without the Loran C or Omega back-up. A sailing yacht travelling at say seven knots will get a position every 10 miles or so which will be sufficient for most coastal navigation requirements, bearing in mind that the DR position will be continuously updated for you. Even if you have got the set and drift badly wrong, the position error between fixes should not get you into trouble unless you are navigating to fine limits.

For powerboats the interval between fixes can cause a problem. At 20 knots there could be 30 miles between fixes and this could lead to considerable deviation from the course before the position is up-dated. The Transit receiver could still be a help in coastal navigation at these speeds, but you must always be conscious of the fix interval and not follow the readings blindly.

The use of Transit can get you into difficulties if you use it to try and make a harbour approach in bad visibility. Here it is important to be aware of the interval between fixes for the particular latitude and to try and avoid any changes in speed, so that both the DR and the fix will be as accurate as possible. The accuracy of both types of fix can deteriorate in harbour approaches because of variations in tidal streams, and the apparently accurate position shown on the display should not be taken at face value, but should be questioned in detail, particularly if you are about to commit yourself to a course which demands navigation to close tolerances.

Modern Transit receivers are built around a powerful micro-processor which carries out the complex calculations necessary to

One of the first Navstar GPS receivers with a full CRT display screen.

determine the yacht's position from the Doppler measurements of the satellite signal. In addition it interprets the signal giving satellite orbit characteristics and from this it can also predict the time of the next satellite pass and its elevation. The spare capacity of the computer is also available for waypoint navigation calculations so that a planned route can be programmed into the receiver and the course and distance to the next waypoint can be called up on the display. Sophisticated receivers will provide both Great circle or rhumbline courses and can be used for all general navigation calculations.

Selecting a suitable Transit receiver can offer a number of alternatives. The cheapest receivers will be single channel receivers which will require course and speed inputs to be inserted manually. From this level, the next stage is automatic input of course and speed combined with the waypoint navigation function. It is useful to get a set with a large waypoint capacity and a memory capable of retaining them so that you do not have to go through the laborious task of inserting the waypoints every time you go to sea.

At the top of the range are the dual channel receivers. The satellites transmit on 150 and 400MHz and by using these two frequencies the effects of refraction can be eliminated, giving a higher degree of accuracy. With an accurate speed input, the errors of the fix can be halved by the use of a dual channel receiver, but the cost is usually more than doubled so that such equipment is not likely to be attractive for the average yachtsman.

The type of display and the control panel should be considered when selecting a suitable receiver. Displays range from a single LED display to a small CRT. The single display shows the latitude and longitude alternatively and is only found on the cheapest receivers. A two line display is the least which should be considered so that the complete position can be displayed. Alternative information will be shown when the appropriate controls are used. The CRT display allows several lines of information but this facility tends to be reflected in the price and the higher power consumption.

The control panel is usually a numeric keyboard with additional keys for the frequently used dedicated functions. Alternatively the number keys will have a dual function and it is important to make sure that the keyboard is easy to use without constant reference to the handbook. The shorthand labelling of keys often leaves a lot to be desired and unless the receiver is used frequently, the handbook has to be constantly consulted. Ideally the keys should have a click or some other positive action so that you know that contact has been made. On a moving yacht it is not always easy to make a positive stroke on the keyboard.

Antenna requirements also have to be considered. Early Transit receiver aerials had a series of spikes around a central pin, a configuration unsuited to sailing yachts. Modern antenna are fully enclosed in a plastic housing and can be easily accommodated on power and sailing yachts. Ideally the antenna should have a clear view around the horizon which means a masthead fitting, but compromise on sailing yachts allows the antenna to be mounted on a short pole mast clipped to the aft pulpit.

The Transit satellite system has recently been upgraded with the addition of three NOVA satellites to the constellation. These new satellites improve the coverage and reduce the interval between fixes. They also have a stronger signal although fully compatible with the existing satellites. Occasions can arise when more than one satellite is available for a position fix and modern receivers will automatically select the best satellite to give the optimum results.

This development of the Transit system is part of a long term plan, but it looks as though the Transit system will be phased out during the mid 1990's when the new Navstar GPS satellite system is fully operational and tried and tested. Whilst existing Transit receivers will still have a potential 10-year life, the time is approaching when the purchase of a Transit receiver will no longer be justified because of the limited availability of the system. Navstar GPS receivers suitable for yacht use are not yet on the market and even if they were, the availability of Navstar GPS is very limited. This puts the use of satellite navigation into limbo to a degree, and the decision as to whether to purchase a Transit receiver or whether to wait for Navstar GPS to become fully operational will be a difficult one to make.

The forecast life of Transit certainly would give a receiver bought now a useful life span in relation to the purchase cost, but the dilemma lies in the fact that Navstar GPS will offer so many advantages over Transit, that it will be hard to live with the shortcomings of Transit once Navstar GPS is available. Like Transit, Navstar GPS is a US Navy development and it is being developed to meet the requirement for a worldwide position-finding system which will be available on a continuous basis and give a high degree of accuracy. Unlike Transit, Navstar GPS will be available for commercial use right from the outset, although commercial users, and that means yachtsmen, will have to make do with a reduced level of accuracy, and there has been discussion about payment for the use of the system.

Navstar GPS will be based on a satellite constellation comprising 18 satellites spaced in six orbital planes inclined at 55 degrees. The orbits will be circular and will have periods of 12 hours. With this configuration, at least four satellites will be in view

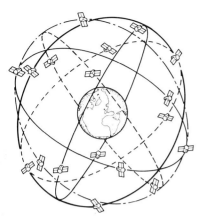

The planned orbits of the 18 satellites of the Navstar GPS system.

of any receiver on the earth's surface at any one time. This will give continuous three-dimensional position finding at all times and whilst the yachtsman may not be interested in knowing his height, the availability of four satellites will be helpful to validate the two-dimensional position.

The test configuration available up till 1987 comprises six satellites and gives two-dimensional position finding in many regions for up to six hours per day. It is planned to start launching the operational satellites in 1986 and the initial constellation development will be planned to give two-dimensional position fixing where it will be most beneficial. By the end of 1987 this two-dimensional position fixing should be available continuously on a worldwide basis and the full 18 satellite constellation will be in position by the end of 1988. These dates assume that there will be no failures, either in the satellites themselves or the Space Shuttle launch vehicle.

The Navstar GPS system will comprise a control segment, a space segment, and the user segment. The control segment will be located in Colorado Springs USA where all the data processing will take place and this will be linked to five widely separated monitor stations. These monitor stations will collect data from the satellites and pass this to the control station which will then calculate the orbits and other criteria. Three of the monitor stations will have ground/satellite links through which the corrections can be entered into the navigational data encoded in the carrier-wave signal transmitted from the satellite.

Each satellite in the system will transmit signals on two frequencies; L1 at 1575.42MHz and L2 at 1227.6MHz. Both of these frequencies will be modulated by the P-code whilst another code, the C/A code, will be transmitted on the L1 frequency only. The P-code will only be available to military and selected civilian users and yachtsmen will only have access to the C/A code. The accuracy available with the P-code could be in the order of 5-10 metres whilst that of the C/A code could be 50 metres but the intention is to intentionally degrade the accuracy of the C/A code so that a nominal 100 metres accuracy will be available.

Positions will be determined from the Navstar GPS by simply measuring the range of the observer from the satellites in view. With the position of the satellites known very accurately, these ranges will provide position lines, with the observer being at the crossing point. Measurement of the ranges will be on a continuous basis so that the position will be continually updated, the complex calculations to translate the ranges into latitude and longitude read-outs being accomplished by the micro-computer built into the onboard receiver.

Most of the major manufacturers are developing receivers for the Navstar GPS. It is anticipated that externally, these receivers will be very similar to those currently available for use with the Transit system. The cost of the first receivers is likely to be high, comparable to the early Transit receivers but with the developments taking place in electronics in general, cost, size and power consumption are expected to reduce, offering the prospect of small hand-held receivers by the mid 1990s. Some observers suggest that these hand-held receivers will be suitable for dinghy use although the need for position finding in dinghies is open to dispute. Low cost yacht receivers should be available by 1990.

There will be a choice between single and multi-channel receivers for the Navstar system. The single channel receivers will have to sample each of the satellites in turn whereas the multi-channel receivers will take them all in together. Multi-channel receivers will be able to offer high accuracy and a constant update in position, but for yacht requirements the single channel receiver will be quite adequate and should perform well within the limits of the degraded signal.

To ease the transition from Transit to Navstar some manufacturers are developing additional circuit boards which can slot into the receiver to give a capability to receive signals and develop positions from either satellite system. This approach may be valid for ship receivers, but the small, cheap yacht receiver is likely to be considered a throw-away item rather than one for up-grading. Because of the higher frequencies used with Navstar the antenna required is likely to be more compact and its mounting position on a yacht will be less critical.

Because no speed or heading input will be required with Navstar receivers, operation will be extremely simple, requiring little more from the operator than switching on and off. It will take a little while for the receiver to get up to date with the satellite characteristics, but once fully initialised, the receiver will give positions of a high order of accuracy on a continuous basis.

The forecast accuracy of Navstar GPS of 100 metres will make the sytem more than adequate for both ocean and coastal navigation. Continuous position fixing to this level of accuracy is a navigator's dream and the system will be unaffected by weather or atmospheric conditions so that a high degree of reliance can be placed on the system.

For precise port-approach navigation, higher levels of accuracy may be demanded, particularly where channel widths are narrow. It could be argued that if the visibility is such that channel markers cannot be seen within the prescribed accuracy limits then navigation should not be attempted anyway, but higher accuracy levels from the Navstar system will be available in sensitive port-approach areas through differential systems.

Differential navigation involves having a Navstar receiver based at a precisely defined location on shore. This allows the errors in the system to be measured very accurately and these same errors will be applicable over the surrounding region. With a differential navigation system the errors are determined continuously through this shore receiver and transmitted out to vessels at sea through a radio link which automatically applies the corrections to the onboard receiver. With differential techniques the accuracy of a Navstar GPS receiver could be as high as 5-10 yards but for yachts the additional cost is unlikely to be justified, and such a sytem is mainly designed for the precise navigation of large ships in narrow channels. Precise position finding, however, is a prerequisite of the Viewnav system of combined electronic chart and radar and differential Navstar systems could be applied here. (see Chapter 8).

Navstar GPS is only one of several new satellite navigation systems being developed or proposed, although it is the furthest advanced. In the Soviet Union, a system very similar to Navstar is being brought into operation on a similar time scale. Called Glonass, this system will operate with 12 satellites and is aimed at providing two-dimensional position fixing rather than the three-dimensional fix of Navstar, but that will be adequate for marine navigation.

The Soviet Union already has the Tsikada satellite navigation system in operation and this is very similar to Transit. Little use of this system has been made outside the vessels of the Soviet Union and it seems unlikely that the introduction of Glonass will have any impact on the yacht market unless the user charges which have been proposed for Navstar GPS by the US Government are implemented. The latest information suggests that these user charges will not be applied so that Glonass will be a non-starter in the yacht market.

The political implications in these nationally-controlled world-wide navigation systems, which have been primarily developed for defence purposes, have led to proposals from the European Space Agency (ESA) for a purely commercial satellite navigation system. By removing the security aspect which has to be built into the defence systems. ESA claim that a cheaper system with very high integrity could be developed offering very precise position finding of less than one metre for those prepared to pay for it and reduced accuracy of 80-100 metres for low-cost receivers.

The concept of an internationally-controlled worldwide satellite navigation system is attractive and Inmarsat, who control international marine satellite communications are the logical body to run such a system. However the impending commissioning of the Navstar system is likely to dampen much of the enthusiasm of the ESA system which is called by the confusing name of Navsat.

Navsat would use a constellation of 24 satellites whilst another proposed satellite navigation system developed in West Germany called Granas proposed a 20-satellite configuration. The main difference between the two systems is the way in which the satellite orbits are determined. Like Navsat, the Granas system would appear to have little chance of becoming operational.

A totally different approach to satellite navigation is found in the Geostar system. This is a purely commercial system aimed at providing very accurate position finding and limited communications on a country or regional basis. Users would pay for the service which would be available for land and air as well as marine users.

Under development by the Geostar Corporation, the Geostar system is very simple. Very powerful computers would be land-based and linked to two satellites which in effect would be simply transponders, linking the control computers to the user's transceiver. Interrogation signals would be sent out from the central computer nominally at 100 times per second. Relayed by the satellites, these would trigger a response from the user's transceiver. Range measurements from the returning signals via the two satellites would be used to compute the user's position by the central computer which would then transmit the position back to the user.

This complex transaction would take place in a fraction of a second and the system would be capable of handling a very large number of users simultaneously. The position accuracy of such a system is claimed to be one metre which would meet the requirements of all forms of transport. The communications link would be fairly basic and would perhaps be limited to emergency and distress working, but combined with the position information this could be a valuable service.

With the positions and track of every user held in the central computer, it becomes possible to develop a collision-avoidance system providing all vessels are linked into the system. Geostar is capable of many interesting developments and if satisfactory commercial funding can be arranged, the system could become operational in the USA in the late 1980s. Commercial viability is only likely in high traffic density areas which could make a similar system practical in Europe.

The introduction of Navstar GPS in 1987 will be a milestone in navigation history. For the first time navigators will have an all-embracing, all-weather navigation system with adequate accuracy. It seems highly probable that it will eventually supercede Loran C and Decca Navigator coverage and closing down dates for the

Loran system have already been announced, although these dates are by no means final. The transition to Navstar will be gradual rather than sudden, particularly for yachtsmen who operate in local waters well served by existing systems. The transition will be made as receivers become due for renewal or as the cost of Navstar receivers comes down.

The prospects for the alternative satellite navigation systems do not look bright apart from Geostar. The uncertainty surrounding these alternative systems does not diminish the fact that yachtsmen will once again be looking to the stars for navigation information, but now it will be the artificial stars which will meet most of the yachtsman's needs as far as position finding is concerned.

A typical Transit satnav receiver for yacht use. Receivers for operating on the Navstar GPS system will eventually come in a similar sized package.

A modern small boat radar which uses a raster scan display with the enclosed antenna unit behind. The display can be mounted in a number of alternative positions to make it convenient to use.

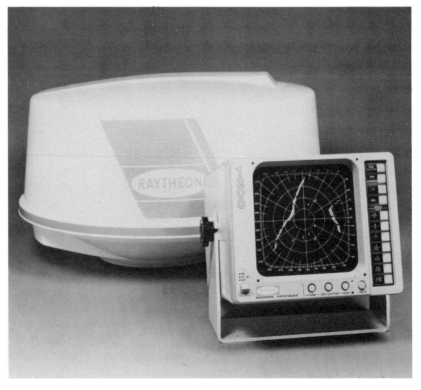

3 Radar to see

Out of all the modern pieces of electronic equipment for yachts, radar is the one which provides the most comprehensive navigation package. It can provide you with your position, it draws up a map of the land around you showing you where you are going and it can show you where other vessels are, thus giving warning about impending collisions. It all sounds too good to be true, and it is, because radar never quite tells the full story. It cannot be relied on to show up everything that is around you, it does not show what is underwater, it is affected by some weather conditions, and the map it shows can be distorted.

Radar promises a lot, but it never quite lives up to its promise. However, the big attraction about radar is that it can provide information for safe navigation in conditions when the yachtsman could find himself in difficulties and it is this that makes radar worthwhile. To give the best performance, the useful information sometimes has to be coaxed out of the set and unlike most modern electronics, the user has to build up a relationship with the radar, to know the area he is working in, and above all, to appreciate the way in which the information is being presented, if it is going to be of use when the going gets tough.

With the map-like display of radar, it is very easy to take what you see at face value; to assume that it is a bird's eye view of the area around you and that the display is comparable to a chart. The radar is not, however, looking down over the area, but is looking out from a position not much higher than your eyes. If you turn round through 360 degrees standing in your yacht, you will get some idea of what the radar is seeing, which usually does not amount to very much at sea. The radar has one big advantage over your eyes and that is its ability to measure distance so that the plan type of display can be used. Some of the things which might appear on a map however, may not show up because of the horizontal view points. This is why you cannot see into the next bay until you are well round the headland, and is why the radar picture may not always correspond with the chart.

The question of interpreting the radar picture correctly is very important. Radar is now a compulsory fitting on most ships and the crew using the radar attend courses on the equipment and this is backed up by regular use. On yachts the approach to radar is much more casual and this can lead to mistakes being made. Radar is the one electronic instrument where a user input is required to get the best out of the radar, and this requires a thorough

A raster scan radar in which the components can be separated to make it easier to fit the units into a confined space. The base unit can be separate from the display and the control panel can be removed and used remotely. Connection is by means of an infra-red link.

understanding of the principles and limitations of the radar as well as practice in fine weather. Only then will you be able to use the equipment with confidence in difficult conditions.

The Principles and Problems of Radar

There are four parts to a yacht radar, although these are generally combined into two packages. The transmitter is usually combined with the antenna which ensures that the maximum radio energy is transmitted from the rotating antenna. The reflected signal returns to the antenna and is directed to the receiver which is usually combined with the display unit.

The transmitter sends out very short pulses at a very high frequency. The rotating antenna directs these pulses around the horizon and they are reflected back from any solid object which they strike. After sending out the pulse the antenna is then open for reception and such is the speed of the radio waves that they can go out and back many miles in the very short space of time in which the antenna faces a particular direction. The returned signals are then processed in the receiver before being displayed in the appropriate position on the display screen.

The length of the transmitted pulse is important because the receiver will not be open for reception until the pulse has been transmitted. We are only talking about micro-seconds here, but the radar pulse travels at the rate of one mile in 6.2 micro-seconds. The shorter the pulse length, the sooner the receiver is open for business and the smaller the dead area around the vessel where no returns can be obtained. Typically a pulse length of 0.1 micro-seconds is used on the shorter radar ranges which is equivalent to about 30 metres. However there is only limited energy in this short pulse and on longer ranges there might not be enough of this energy reflected to reach the receiver so a longer pulse is used on longer ranges, typically having a length of 0.5 micro-seconds which increases the dead area to 150 metres. This switch from one pulse length to another is done automatically.

Another point to consider is the pulse repetition frequency (PRF). There is no point in sending out another pulse from the antenna until the returning pulses from the last transmission have all returned. On short ranges a higher PRF can be tolerated because the pulses do not have so far to travel. This higher PRF gives a better chance of detecting small targets. On short ranges the PRF is typically around 2500 pulses per second whilst this figure is usually halved on longer ranges.

The performance of a radar set can be affected by a number of factors and these must be borne in mind when interpreting the display. The pulse length, apart from determining the size of the dead area around the immediate vicinity of the vessel, also determines whether the radar will be able to discriminate between two targets on the same bearing. If these two targets are closer than the 150 metres which is the distance relative to the time taken for the pulse to pass, then the two targets will appear as one. This range discrimination is not usually very critical as far as yachts are concerned and the changing pattern of targets will also show up the hidden target.

A low radar scanner on a yacht may allow large waves to interrupt the radar beam and cause temporary blank areas on the screen.

Perhaps more critical is bearing discrimination which is determined by the beam width of the transmissions from the antenna. Ideally the beam should be pencil thin so that it only picks up targets on the specific bearing. In practice the beam may have a three degree width so that any targets within this sector will show up on the same bearing. The effect will be magnified at longer ranges and this is why distant targets tend look longer on the display. Two targets close together at the same range will be shown as one target if they come within the limits of the same radar beam.

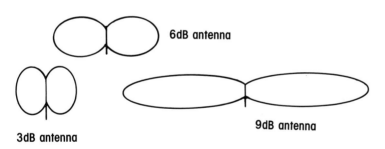

6dB antenna

3dB antenna

9dB antenna

Signal radiation patterns from different VHF antennae. The higher the gain, the narrower the radiated signal beam.

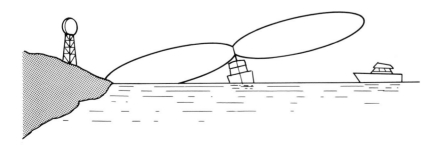

A very high gain antenna with its narrow beam will not accommodate the movement of a yacht at sea.

Whilst the radar beam is made as narrow as possible in the horizontal plane, and most of the energy is concentrated in the main beam, it will have much weaker signals radiating out on different bearings. These side lobes are only a problem at shorter ranges and fortunately at these ranges, the returns from the main beam are strong so that the gain can be reduced and these side echoes more or less eliminated. They may be a problem when using the radar in built-up areas, but modern antenna design has almost eliminated this problem.

With heavy rolling, the horizontal beam width of the radar beam may be insufficient to cover the whole span of the rolling angle and the picture may be temporarily lost.

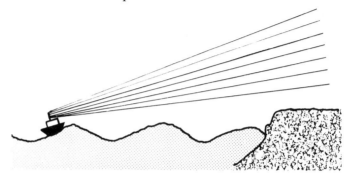

In the vertical plane, the radar beam has to be made much wider so that when the boat rolls, part of the beam is still pointing towards the horizon. The vertical beam width is normally around 30 degrees with the horizontal line at the middle of the beam. Even with this beam width, it is still possible for the beam to lift over the horizon in heavier rolls or when a sailing yacht heels with the wind and this will be apparent by blank sectors on the display. Hopefully these will only be temporary blanks.

The radar looks outward horizontally from a comparatively low viewpoint and, if a big sea is running, it is very possible for a wave to cut off the radar beam and hence any target return from behind the wave. This can also cause blank sectors on the display, but again they will be temporary and the picture will return when the yacht is on top of the wave.

It is the reflections from waves which cause sea clutter.

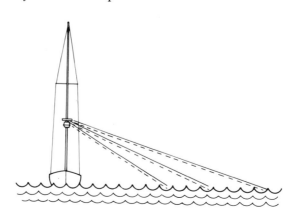

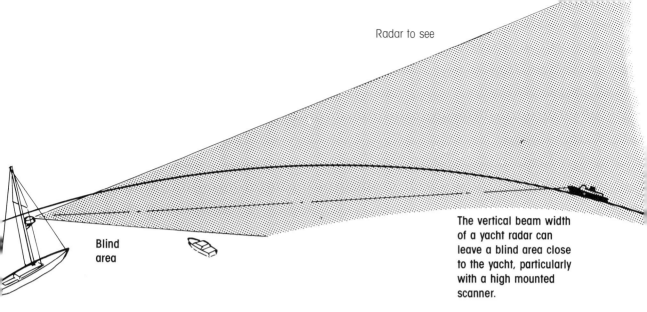

Radar to see

The vertical beam width of a yacht radar can leave a blind area close to the yacht, particularly with a high mounted scanner.

Blind area

All of these factors have to be borne in mind when interpreting the picture on the radar display. The display will show returns from any target which comes into the radar beam provided it will reflect the radar pulse. Rocky coastlines provide the strongest returns whilst gently shelving beaches do not show up well. Large steel ships are good targets as are built up areas on shore, but glass fibre yachts are poor targets. These and other small targets such as small buoys can be lost in the return from waves, because water also reflects the radar pulse.

Returns from waves will be worst in strong winds because of the vertical wave faces which provide the strongest returns. This clutter, as it is called, will be more obvious to windward because of the steeper wave faces. Clutter controls are fitted to reduce the sensitivity of the radar on a graduating scale away from the antenna, but this control is no respecter of targets and is just as likely to cut out small boats and other weak targets. However the weak targets tend to provide a constant return which gives a persistent 'paint' on the display whilst the wave returns are more random. Sophisticated processing techniques in modern radars demand that a target shows up on two or three successive antenna rotations before it is confirmed as a target and shown on the display. This enhancement technique is one of the major advances in modern radar technology and can help to find small targets in rough seas.

Modern Radar Equipment

Modern electronic techniques are being used increasingly to improve the performance and presentation of small boat radars. The old type of radial scan radar display is steadily being replaced with raster scan displays which give much greater flexibility in the

A colour radar display which uses colour primarily to distinguish different features on the screen. The lower unit can be mounted separate from the display to simplify installation.

way in which the raw radar signal can be processed and in which information can be presented on the screen.

The radial display is rotated in unison with the radar antenna and acts as the time base for measuring the range of targets. The scan starts out from the centre of the screen at the same time as the pulse leaves the antenna, but travels at half the speed in terms of time. This is because the pulse has to go out and back from the target and so this time has to be halved on the display. The returning signal from a target is shown as a bright spot on the radar display at the appropriate distance and bearing from the centre.

Although still used for small boat radars, the radial scan is being replaced by the raster scan display where the scan moves across the screen in a series of horizontal lines. This means that points on the screen can be defined in terms of X-Y co-ordinates allowing numerical information to be displayed as well as the radar picture itself. Radar sets using this type of display are software-based instead of the earlier hardware-based equipment. They use a micro-processor with a sophisticated software programme which takes the raw radar information and processes it in a variety of ways to give a radar picture which is much easier to interpret and is much better suited to small boat applications.

The radar screen is akin to a TV tube, but uses a higher definition, with more horizontal lines so that the detail is clearer. The raw radar information has first to be transformed from the radial to the horizontal scan and then the returning signals are enhanced to make them stand out better from the background. This enables the display to be bright enough to view in daylight without the need for shielding — a great advantage in a small boat. Some screening from bright sunlight may be necessary, but the open type of display can be watched by two or more people at once if necessary.

The use of the software control means that many of the setting up procedures are now automatic. The tuning of the receiver to the transmitted signal is maintained at the optimum setting, the centreing is automatic and the heading-marker lines up automatically. The gain and brilliance still have to be set up to suit the conditions whilst the sea clutter control can be automatic or manual. The memory facilities of the software programme can allow the picture to be frozen which can ease the interpretation of difficult situations.

Range and bearing measurements are much easier with the software-oriented radar. With the radial scan radar, bearing cursors were usually mechanical whilst variable range markers (VRM) were an expensive luxury usually omitted from the cheaper radars, which relied on fixed range-rings for range measurement. Modern small boat radars have fully electronic bearing cursors and VRMs as well as the fixed range-rings and these can increase the capability and ease of use of the equipment.

The VRM can be used to establish a guard zone so that any target crossing this line triggers off an alarm signal. When close to land such a guard zone would not be selective enough and manufacturers are now fitting two bearing cursors and two VRMs so that a guard zone can be defined both by range and bearing to cover a specific area. Guard zones such as this can be more trouble than they are worth if they are prone to false alarms, so it is usual for any target crossing the line to have to come up on several successive sweeps in order for the alarm to be triggered. This is a similar technique to that used for coping with sea clutter and demonstrates the flexibility offered with this type of radar. The readout for the bearing cursors and VRMs is shown in digital form on the display. The corners of the square screen are usually used for this display and some radars allow for specific targets to be identified and even tracked with target information being displayed in a similar way.

The efficiency of a small boat radar should not be judged by the stated maximum range of the radar. A radar with a range extending out to 48 miles on the display is no guarantee that targets will be detected at this range. Even if they were, it would be very difficult to identify them in any positive way and there is little point in having a yacht radar with a range of even 24 miles. In practice, the 12 mile range will probably be the maximum used for normal navigation and is the limit at which land features can be identified positively. For collision avoidance the three mile range is most commonly used.

A useful feature found on some radars is the ability to offset the centre. You are not usually so concerned with what is happening astern, and by offsetting the centre an extended range ahead can be seen. This can provide a good compromise in the display and can be useful for general navigation as well as collision avoidance.

When making a landfall, the high ground behind the coast may be the first thing to show up on the screen. Only as you close on the land will the coastline itself show up and will you be able to make a positive identification. This is because of the curvature of the earth's surface, although under some atmospheric conditions the radar beam can be bent or refracted downwards to follow more closely the earth's surface. Similarly some conditions will refract the beam upwards, reducing the maximum detection range.

The radar display is normally prsented with the yacht's head upwards. This is a logical presentation and makes interpretation quite easy with practice. Some radars allow a compass input so that the top of the display can be north and the display then is much more comparable to the chart. With such a compass-stabilised display, compass bearings can be read directly from the bearing cursor, otherwise, the compass course has to be applied to make the bearings useable on the chart.

Installation

Correct installation of the display and scanner can go a long way to getting the best out of this equipment which relies quite a lot on the human interpretation to produce meaningful information. In considering the display, it should have priority over other equipment so that the operator can use and operate it comfortably, even when the boat is tossing around. Most displays are susceptible to water so they should be mounted in a protected position, down below on a sailing yacht, or in the wheelhouse of a motor yacht or motor sailer. Some radars have a remote control panel which can be mounted separately from the display itself and this can give greater flexibility in installing the equipment.

In fog you may have to spend long periods watching the radar display closely. This can be trying and a lot of thought should go into finding the optimum location. You need to get fairly close to the screen to pick out small targets and good handholds are necessary in order to locate yourself steadily in front of the screen.

You have the choice of looking down into the radar display when it is mounted horizontally or looking directly at it with a vertical mount. In some respects the horizontal mount is more logical because the display is rather like a chart, but you have to stand up to watch this type of display and the vertical screen or slightly angled screen is the one usually chosen because it takes up less space on a small boat. A vertical screen is best at, or below, eye level and it can be a strain watching a screen placed up under the deckhead, although this is often a convenient place for installation.

The radar display should not be too close to the magnetic compass, with two feet probably being the minimum distance. The radar is a large piece of equipment to fit on a small boat and compass and radar can compete for priority. Mounting the radar antenna can also create difficulties, particularly on a sailing yacht and careful thought and design is required to get the optimum position.

Two types of antenna are available, the open and closed types. In the open type, the revolving antenna itself is fully weather-proofed, but this type is only really suited to motor yachts where ropes and sails are not likely to interfere with its operation. The enclosed type sites the revolving antenna inside a plastic cover which protects it and at the same time allows the antenna and associated equipment to be much lighter as it is not directly exposed to wind and weather. Much less power is required to turn the antenna — an important consideration on sailing yachts.

The plastic dome does not obstruct the radar beam, but it does tend to limit the size of antenna which can be accommodated. The length of the antenna is critical to the performance of the radar, the longer antenna producing a much narrower beam which increases the range of detection and also the discrimination. This must, however, be weighed against the installation problems on a small craft and enclosed types are usually two feet in length whilst the open type of scanner can range up to 12 feet, but three or four feet is normal for motor yacht installations.

Wheelhouse top or masts are normally used for the antenna siting in motor yachts. There should be a clear view all round but if there are obstructions, these should be astern. The antenna can be mounted off-centre without problems.

On sailing yachts there are three main alternative positions, on the mast, on the coachroof or on a short dedicated mast aft. The choice will depend on the particular layout. The masthead is rarely used because other antenna have priority, the radar antenna is a large unit to fit so high up and servicing can be difficult. Halfway up the mast is a good compromise, but it may interfere with the smooth tacking of the jib. Halfway up the mizzen is a better position if the yacht has a mizzen, but the dedicated short mast aft makes a good substitute on sloop-rigged yachts and keeps the antenna well out of harm's way. The coachroof must be considered a last resort both because it is very low down and because it will take up valuable deck space. A protective grill over the dome may be necessary to prevent ropes getting fouled up in it.

Colour Radar

The standard radar display is monochrome, normally green or orange against a black background. The advent of colour tubes with good discrimination has led to the development of colour radar displays which on the surface appear to be a major step forward, but which in reality do not offer any major advantage at the present stage of development.

Colour can be used in several ways with a radar display. Colour in its simplest form is used as an extension of the monochrome display, with the radar targets shown in one single colour against a contrasting background of another colour. It is possible to vary the colour combinations to give the optimum display for the ambient light conditions. On this type of display further use of colour is

Certain atmospheric conditions can cause the beam to be bent upwards or downwards at long ranges, causing either a loss of targets or targets to be shown at longer than expected ranges.

At long ranges only the tops of mountains may be detected because of the curvature of the earth.

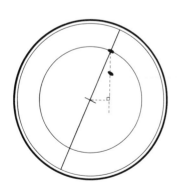

If a ship target opens out from the bearing cursor which was placed through its original position then the ship will be passing clear, but beware of only a small change in the bearing.

found by showing range rings or VRMs in a third colour and some displays incorporate a facility for drawing lines on the display to indicate shallow water areas or traffic lanes. These are also shown in a separate colour.

With this type of receiver, colour is only used to enhance the clarity of the display, but other radars use colour to denote the strength of the returned signal. Red is used for the strongest returns and green is usually reserved for the weakest. Whilst it appears logical to identify targets by the strength of their return in this way, it has little practical value and tends to highlight those targets which are often of little interest. The strong red returns from the land tend to dominate the screen making it harder to detect the weaker green targets. It would make more sense to reverse this colour coding, because it is often the weak targets which are of most interest.

Colour radar has great potential and is in its early stages of development. With sophisticated processing techniques it should be possible to make colour displays play a much more useful role and one which justifies the considerably higher cost of the equipment.

Radar Performance

The detection range of a target by radar depends not only on the height of the target above the observer's horizon, but also on the amount of the radar pulse which is reflected back. The strength of the radar pulse diminishes with distance from the antenna and when it strikes a target only a portion of the energy is reflected back. How much depends on the aspect of the target, its surface texture, the type of material, the angle of the surface to the vertical, and its area.

Metal and rock are the best reflectors; hard material which absorbs very little of the energy. Softer surfaces such as sand or mud are poor reflectors whilst vegetation, timber and fabrics reflect very little which is why radar can work well on a sailing yacht. A vertical surface at right angles to the beam is a good reflector whilst a sloping surface such as a beach will tend to dissipate the energy with little return to the antenna. A broken surface, however, will reflect a useful proportion of the energy because the many angled surface makes a good reflector.

Ships will generally return a strong signal, detectable on a small boat radar at over 10 miles. Smaller ships may show up between 5 and 10 miles. Lightvessels and isolated lighthouses will have about the same range and if fitted with a radar transponder or beacon can be readily identified from adjacent shipping by the special signal shown on the screen.

Buoys and small craft are not generally very good radar targets. Fibreglass and wooden yachts are some of the worst targets and which is why many are equipped with radar reflectors which can considerably enhance the return. Detection without a radar reflector may be only 2 miles and the return may be easily lost in sea clutter, whilst the radar reflector should make detection possible at 4 to 5 miles and will certainly give a stronger return to show up amongst the sea clutter. Even if you have radar, you want other craft to pick your vessel up on their radar so a radar reflector should be standard equipment.

Future Radar Developments

Radar is still comparatively new for yachts and its present popularity is largely the result of modern electronics which allow compact reliable equipment to be developed. The switch to software orientated radar has been one of the most significant developments to take place in small boat radars and the use of software programmes is still in its infancy.

The small boat radar market is still in its infancy and lags well behind the equipment available for big ships. For years small boat radars have been based on the big ship concept with many of the desirable features removed to keep costs down. The small boat radar market is very cost sensitive, but with the introduction of software orientated radar, the door is opened for the use of sophisticated radar concepts at moderate prices. This development can be justified because of the large market for small boat radars compared with that for shipping.

The introduction of true motion radar for yachts will be one of the first developments. With it the yacht moves across the screen and the coastline remaining stationary. Apart from making a more realistic presentation, such a display also shows moving targets on their natural courses. Current displays show the relative motion where other vessels move with a combination of their own course and speed and that of your own vessel which stays still at the centre of the screen.

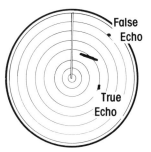

The radar beam can be reflected off a nearby vertical face and produce a false target on the screen. As this will show on the screen behind the vertical face it should not cause much concern.

Reflections of the radar beam can also occur from fittings on the yacht and here a false target could cause problems. The false target will always be in line with the mast or other reflecting surface.

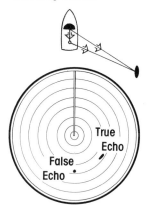

Diagramatic view of a satellite surveillance system which uses synthetic aperture radar to track vessels at sea.

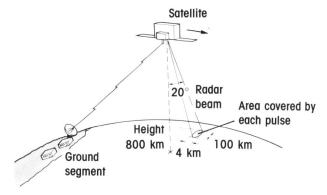

Satellite

20° Radar beam

Area covered by each pulse

Height 800 km

100 km

4 km

Ground segment

True motion is a big step forward and the software can also be used to track approaching targets to give warning of impending collision. Further into the future is the possibility of the computer giving advice about altering course, yet another step down the slippery slope towards automation. As electronic chart displays gain ground then chart and radar could be combined. Link in a position finding system and you have the complete navigation system in one unit. With so much information to display on one screen, colour will be essential to make interpretation easy.

Radar Detectors

The ability to detect the bearing of the radar signals of an approaching ship could be a help when navigating in fog. Whilst very much a second best, a radar detector may be better than nothing, but must be used with caution and is certainly no substitute for a good look-out.

A radar detector is rather like an RDF set, usually hand held. First of all it will indicate that there are radar transmissions in the vicinity and secondly, will give an approximate bearing of the radar transmitter when the instrument is pointed towards it. By observation over a period it is possible to get some idea what the other vessel is doing and the strength of the signal gives some idea of the closeness, but the absence of any clear-cut picture can make any sort of avoiding action difficult to judge.

Possibly the best use of this type of instrument is its ability to give a warning about other shipping, but remember that not all vessels have radar. Signals from shore radar which might cause confusion will also be picked up. With the advent of low cost radars, these detectors are disappearing from the market and are unlikely to have much relevance in the future.

The viewing hood required on older radars which were not equipped with daylight viewing. This greatly restricted the installation which had to provide for comfortable viewing.

4 The old faithful —
Radio Direction Finding

Like most electronic navigation instruments, the principle of the radio direction finder (RDF) is simple. A transmitting station or radio beacon sends out a non-directional signal, and by means of a directional aerial on board the vessel and a simple receiver, a bearing can be obtained. If two or more bearings on different stations are used, a fix is obtained.

RDF was the first electronic navigation system to be developed and whilst it is simple in principle there are several complications which can affect the accuracy of the position obtained. Because of this and because some of the simpler receiving sets require a fair degree of operator skill, the RDF is often ignored in favour of other more complicated and expensive systems. RDF in it simplest form is the cheapest of the electronic position finding systems for coastal work, and operating skill is quickly obtained with practice. The purist who disdains other forms of electronic position finding accepts RDF because operator skills play a large part in obtaining a usable position and the system provides a useful back up in poor visibility.

Radio beacons are of five main types:

1　Beacons transmitting continuously in all conditions. These are often in groups of up to six which transmit on the same frequency one after the other for a six minute period, identifying themselves by Morse code letter signals. This grouping reduces the demand on radio frequencies and at the same time enables an operator to obtain three or more bearings from convenient beacons without retuning the receiver.

2　Beacons similar to those in group 1 but which transmit only in fog. These tend to be of limited range and there is always the possibility that the navigator will be in fog, yet the station will not be transmitting because it is clear only a short distance away.

3　Aircraft beacons. Many airfields have radio beacons for aircraft use. Those close to the coast can be used equally well by vessels at sea. These beacons operate on a higher frequency than most marine beacons, and it may not always be possible to receive some of them on standard equipment.

4　Calibration beacons. These have a limited range and are primarily intended to enable vessels to calibrate their RDF sets to check fixed errors. Calibration beacons are usually situated near large ports in a position where a vessel can steam right round them. While designed primarily for calibration there is no reason why they should not be used for navigation purposes.

Radio beacons are listed in the British Admiralty List of Radio Signals Volume 11, and the US Coast Guard Lights List. In addition there are many other publications such as Almanacs which list the beacons in particular areas.

The lists give full details about the type of signal, the position of the beacon, the range, and the sequence in relation to other beacons, in fact all you need to know to obtain bearings.

Using bearings

The ranges given for beacons vary considerably. Those marking landfall points, such as Ushant off the coast of Brittany or the Ambrose Light Station, have a range of over 100 miles. Other beacons which are used more for coastal navigation may be of 50-mile range, while beacons used on harbour approaches and similar local applications may be of only 10-mile range. The ranges stated are only approximate and will vary according to atmospheric conditions, but as a general rule any bearing from a beacon over 50 miles away must be treated with caution.

The location of beacons is such that it should normally be possible to find at least two beacons within a 50-mile radius particularly when making a landfall, which is when fixes are most required. Bearings from two beacons will give two position lines and where these cross will give the position. With two bearings there is no knowing whether any error has crept in, unless soundings or some other information can be used as a check. For this reason three bearings should be used whenever possible so that some idea of the accuracy of the resulting fix can be obtained.

A one degree error in a bearing of a beacon 60 miles away will produce a one mile error in the position; this will reduce to 200 yards or so at six miles which is more acceptable. It is also much easier to get a reliable bearing from a close beacon than a distant one, and the degree of accuracy in the bearing is likely to be better because the null point is easier to distinguish.

A one degree error in a bearing of a beacon 60 miles away will produce a one mile error in the position.

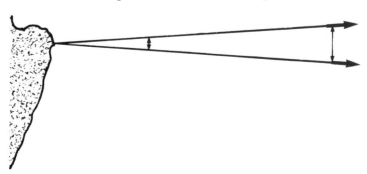

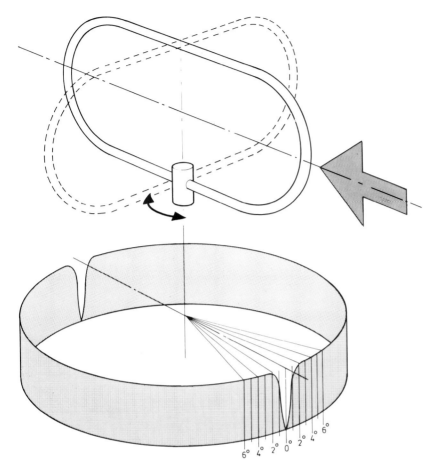

The shaded circle shows the level of an RDF signal with the null or low point occurring sharply when the antenna is directly in line with the beacon.

The null point is the bearing where the signal from the beacon is at its weakest. The RDF set could be designed so that the bearing of the strongest point of the signal could be measured, but it has been found that it is easier to distinguish a minimum rather than a maximum point. Special circuits in the RDF receiver make the cut-off at the null point as sharp as possible.

The variation in the signal strength received is caused by the directional antenna. Three main types are used: the fixed loop, the rotating loop, and the ferrite rod. The last two operate on a similar principle, and the ferrite rod is gaining in popularity as it is more compact than the loop. It is used on all of the portable DF sets. Similar antenna are used on portable transistor radios which are well known for their directional properties.

When either the loop or the ferrite rod antenna is placed so that it is pointing in the direction of the beacon, it picks up the maximum signal. When it is turned, the received signal will gradually diminish until it is at a minimum when the aerial is at right angles to the direction of the beacon. The skill in using DF set lies in identifying this minimum or null point with sufficient accuracy. This is largely a matter of experience. In practice, the null point may be several degrees wide, the width increasing with the distance from the station. It is then a matter of rotating the antenna a few degrees each way and finding the positions on each side of the null where the signal can just be heard. The required bearing is then a mean of these two points.

Having thus obtained the bearing, it has to be corrected in various ways before it can be laid off on the chart. Firstly, it has to be corrected for any fixed errors, rather like a magnetic compass has to be corrected for deviation. These errors are found by 'swinging' the vessel in a similar method to compass adjusting.

Errors and Calibration

Even the most refined DF set needs to be calibrated, if the DF bearings obtained are to be of much use for navigation. Using an uncalibrated DF set is like using an uncorrected compass; a waste of time and a possible danger. Calibration requires the use of a beacon which transmits continuously, and the boat is swung so that the error can be tested on different bearings relative to the ship's head. In this respect, DF calibration differs from compass calibration. With a compass the error is checked on the different heading directions. The errors on a DF set will vary relative to the ship's head, that is to say the error of a bearing 40 degrees on the bow will be different to the error on a bearing which is 80 degrees on the bow on the same heading.

Errors are caused by magnetic metal fittings on the boat such as rigging, stanchions and even window frames. These also pick up the radiated signal from the beacon and re-radiate it causing errors. These can often be reduced by breaking up continuous metal loops on the rigging through fitting insulators, but careful siting of the DF aerial is equally important. This is where a fixed loop on the masthead has distinct advantages as it is likely to be fairly free from error.

Having found a calibration beacon the next step will depend on the type of set. For a portable set, it is as well to compare the compass readings with those of the boat's compass to make sure that it is free from error. If any DF compass errors are found then try a new position for operating the set. There is no point in checking DF errors until the DF compass errors have been eliminated or at least identified.

From this point on, the procedures are similar except that with the fixed set you will need someone to take compass bearings of the beacon station as you take DF bearings. Rotate the boat through 360 degrees, preferably taking a bearing every 10 degrees of swing. Hopefully, the compass bearing, after allowing for corrections, and the DF bearing should read the same. If the DF bearing reads higher than the compass bearing, then the correction will have a minus sign and vice versa.

From the errors found it is possible to make up a deviation curve or table. The curve plotted against the angle relative to the ship's head should be smooth. Any errors which are at variance to this curve should be checked again. The deviation table is used in a similar way to a compass deviation card, but appropriate errors are applied to the bearing relative to the vessel's head.

Before we leave the question of errors, there are three other factors which can affect the accuracy of the bearings obtained. Not much can be done about them except to be aware of them and to use any bearing obtained under these circumstances with a great deal of caution.

The first is the refraction caused to the transmitted signal as it is passed from land to sea. This is a similar phenomenon to the refraction of light when it passes from air to water. It is not generally a problem for marine radio beacons, which are usually situated close to the shore anyway. It can affect the bearing if land intervenes between the beacon and the receiver or if the bearing line runs parallel or nearly parallel to the coast. It is because of refraction that the use of aircraft beacons should be treated with some caution. They are located for the convenience of aircraft and no consideration is given to the refraction that might occur with marine use. Marine beacons are normally situated at lighthouses or lightvessels, which depend on a clear view over the sea. Refraction will be most apparent when sailing close to the coast, but hopefully there will be other ways of checking your position in this situation.

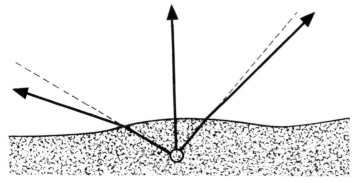

The way in which a signal from a radio beacon can be distorted if it passes over land at an angle. This will only be a problem if the land path is at least two or three miles long.

The second source of error is night effect. In spite of its name, it is most apparent around dawn and dusk, but it also occurs during the night. The reason for the error is fairly technical, but it can be recognised by an unsteady null point and a fluctuation of the signal. In a small boat which is swinging about, it is not so easy to recognise an unsteady null point and the best way of avoiding the error is not to use DF bearings at dawn and dusk, and to restrict the range of bearings used at night to 25 miles if possible. Similar effects are found with the third cause of error, electrical storms, when radio bearings should not be relied on.

When bearings are taken from beacons over 50 miles away, a further correction may have to be applied. This is the half-convergency, the technical name for the fact that radio transmissions follow a great circle bearing which on the normal chart comes out as a shallow curve. The error is small unless the beacon and the ship lie east and west of each other. Even then it will only be in the order of one degree over a distance of 60 miles in the higher latitudes. For most practical purposes it can be ignored but details can be found in most books of nautical tables.

DF does not provide information in the same simple way of the echo sounder. Rather the information has to be coaxed out of it, and accuracy depends a great deal on the skill of the operator. If the trouble is taken to practise and obtain the required skills, then a great deal of useful information can be obtained, often when the navigator has no other information at his disposal, and a relatively low cost in equipment.

Types of RDF Receivers

RDF receivers fall into two main categories; those that use fixed aerials and those that are portable. There is no clear superiority of one over the other and the trend is certainly towards portable RDF, perhaps reflecting its role as a piece of stand-by navigation equipment, but also reflecting the difficulty in finding a suitable location for a fixed antenna on a modern yacht.

The fixed loop DF receivers are often linked into the SSB communications receiver which is tuned to the appropriate beacon frequency. The fixed loop comes in two types, one having two loops set at right angles to each other and the other having a rotating loop. The fixed loop type is usually used in conjunction with an automatic RDF. Modern types automatically display the bearing of a transmission, but are expensive and rarely found on yachts.

The rotating loop is used in much the same way as the portable DF. The loop is rotated to find the null. One of the main advantages of both the fixed and rotating types of antenna is that they have a fixed location in the yacht and so their errors can be quantified quite accurately. The bearing obtained is relative to the yacht's heading and the compass heading, deviation and variation have to be applied to convert this into a true bearing which can be laid off on the chart.

A modern RDF portable receiver where the frequency can be accurately dialled. Because the built-in compass is not corrected, this receiver should only be used in areas away from magnetic influence.

The fixed loop type of RDF allows the navigator to take his bearings in relative comfort down below, whilst the portable RDF should be used up on deck in order to reduce the errors. The portable receiver will work down below quite happily on fibreglass or wooden-hulled yachts but unless it has been calibrated for this position, considerable errors are likely to creep in. These errors will apply to both the DF bearing and the compass if the latter is built into the receiver.

The simple type of portable RDF receiver which comprises a manually tuned radio receiver with built-in aerial and compass has now been largely superceded by sophisticated portable units which use micro-processor control to give much more precise tuning and compass information. These help to simplify the process of taking the bearing, particularly if you are taking bearings of beacons in different frequencies, but at the end of the day it is the operator who has to decide where the null position is. Hearing is still one of the best ways of identifying the null, but meters are also available which help to remove some of the skill required. Electronic identification of the null point is a growing feature of modern RDF receivers and fully automatic receivers are available but tend to be very expensive. Because of the lack of operator involvement in taking the bearing, it may be difficult to judge how much reliance can be placed on it.

The use of a compass built into the portable RDF removes one step in the calculation chain because, as you find the null point, it is a simple matter to read off the compass bearing. This compass, however, is not corrected and the best you can do to enhance the accuracy is to make sure that the compass is used as far away from any magnetic influence as possible. It is also difficult to calibrate a portable RDF receiver with any degree of accuracy because it is rarely used in the same place on the yacht each time. The answer here is to try and use the receiver at a point as far away from the rigging and masts as possible to reduce their influence.

In rough conditions, it may not be practical or safe to stand in an exposed position to take bearings and accuracy can be reduced. Add to this the possible unsteadiness of the compass card in these conditions and accurate bearings are not likely, but they should not necessarily be discarded. The limitations of the accuracy should be appreciated when using the information although it is better to know your position to within 5 miles than not know it at all.

Even with the fixed type of antenna, accuracy may be suspect because you have to apply the vessel's head to the relative DF bearing. In a yacht tossing about at sea the compass card may swing considerably and it is not always easy to establish a mean at the moment the bearing is taken. On balance the errors of both the

A VHF direction finder which will automatically display the relative bearing of any VHF transmission received. It is designed to be linked to a VHF receiver.

A radio compass which is similar to an RDF receiver, but shows the relative bearing of the transmission on a dial. To obtain a bearing which can be plotted on a chart, the yacht's heading has to be applied.

fixed and portable types of DF are likely to be much the same for yacht use and RDF bearings should always be treated with caution, but they can provide navigation information when visual methods are not available. With increasingly automatic types of RDF receivers coming onto the market there is always a worry that the information they produce will be believed implicitly and possible errors will be ignored. Automation of the receiver will not remove the basic errors of the system.

The radio compass is an extension of the RDF system which enables you to home in on a transmitted signal. Although primarily designed for aircraft use as a homing device, it can be used on yachts. It is essentially an automatic RDF requiring a fixed double loop, but it should be used cautiously because there is no indication of distance off and there will always be something solid to hit at the end of the run.

VHF DF

A comparatively recent innovation which has developed from the widespread use of VHF for marine communications is the use of direction finding in conjunction with VHF. Equipment is now on the market which allows bearings to be taken automatically of VHF transmissions although no specific VHF radio beacons have been established. This equipment, however, could have a value in navigation as it allows bearings to be obtained of known shore stations.

The DF equipment links into a VHF receiver or it can be self-contained. Once the appropriate channel has been selected, operation is largely automatic. The bearing of the transmission is indicated on a dial. The bearing of each transmission on the chosen frequency is shown and the response is virtually immediate. Probably the biggest drawback with this type of equipment is the size of the special antenna required which makes it difficult to install on a yacht. Comprising four vertical dipoles mounted in a square formation, the antenna has to be placed in a clear position at the top of the mast and few yachts would like to dedicate this position to a VHF DF antenna.

The use of this equipment is largely restricted to sport and commercial fishermen who want to know where their competitors are fishing, but it also plays an important role in search and rescue.

Another type of VHF DF is OMNI which was developed primarily for aircraft use but is used for marine navigation in some parts of the world. Like all VHF transmissions the range of OMNI is little better than line-of-sight between the respective antenna. All the transmitters for OMNI are located at airports so only those close to the sea are usable for marine operators, but special marine receivers have been developed.

The transmitted signal of OMNI has two parts. One is transmitted from a fixed antenna similar to ordinary DF and the second is transmitted from a rotating directional antenna. The receiver measures the phase difference between the two signals and the readout is given as a magnetic bearing from the transmitter. A continuous readout is available and high accuracy is possible, but distortion can occur if the transmitter is some way inland.

Radio Lighthouses

There has been limited development of radio lighthouses which enable a bearing of a station to be determined using a simple receiver. They operate on VHF frequencies and so have a range limited to 20-30 miles. After tuning in to the frequency, the observer waits for a long dash and then counts the short dashes until a null or momentary pause is heard. He then counts the remaining short dashes until the long dash is heard. The double count acts as a check.

Each short dash represents about 2 degrees and the long dash is the reference direction, usually north. After the count it is a simple matter to convert it into a bearing from the radio lighthouse. These lighthouses usually operate over a only a limited arc to seaward

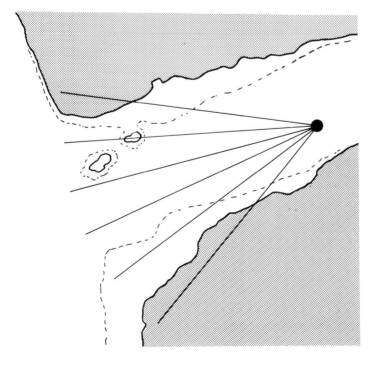

Typical signal counts for a radio lighthouse can determine direction in an approach channel.

thus reducing the count, and the signal is preceded by an identification code. The concept of these radio lighthouses is excellent but they have only been established at a few stations in Europe. Full details of the signals can be found in almanacs and official lists of radio stations.

Another form of radio lighthouse, again with limited application, is rather like an aircraft landing signal. The aim is to provide a radio beam which can keep a vessel on a fixed bearing in a narrow channel. When the vessel is on the correct bearing a steady signal is heard, but wander to left or right and the signal changes in a distinctive way as a warning.

RDF for Search and Rescue

Although the role of RDF for general yacht navigation is diminishing as more sophisticated and accurate position finding systems take over, it still plays a very important role in search and rescue. This role has grown now that most yachts are fitted with VHF radio and can be a tremendous help in locating a casualty. SAR aircraft, helicopters and lifeboats are being equipped with VHF DF sets to enable them to home in on a casualty and many Coast Guard stations on shore are similarly fitted.

One bearing of a casualty can narrow down the search area considerably, whilst cross bearings can pinpoint the position accurately. These faciliites emphasise the vital importance of VHF radio for yachts and the system could be used in reverse to provide the yacht with its position. This must not be considered a routine method of position fixing, the authorities would not want to encourage this type of general use, but in an emergency where an inexperienced crew might find themselves lost at sea, or other equipment has failed, it could provide an essential position fix to get you home.

The emergency services also use RDF on medium frequencies for casualty location, but fewer yachts are fitted with SSB radios which make position fixing possible. The same potential, however, exists and both methods provide reassuring coverage for yachts and other craft in emergencies. In the Great Lakes, the Canadian authorities are experimenting with a computer-controlled plotting system which automatically plots the position of signals received at three carefully located antenna. This can speed up the process and may indicate the route of future developments, but manual plotting is the general method in use today.

5 The lead and the log, also compasses, and autopilots

The echo sounder is the only navigation instrument which looks underwater. You could establish the water depth by first finding the yacht's position and then reading the depth off the chart. The echo sounder, however, gives a real time reading of the depth and so provides a valuable check on the other navigation systems. It also provides great reassurance because most of the navigation dangers facing yachts lie under the water. It should nevertheless be remembered that the echo sounder only shows what is immediately under the yacht and not what lies ahead.

Principles of Operation

The basic principle of operation is the same for all echo sounders. A sound pulse is sent out from a transducer in the bottom of the boat. This sound pulse strikes the sea bed and is reflected back upwards where it is received by the same or a second transducer. The echo sounder unit initiates the sending of the sound pulse and then measures the time taken between its transmission and reception. Knowing the speed of sound in water, it is a simple matter to find the distance travelled by the sound, half of which will be the depth.

The traditional towed log in modern form with the option of a cockpit dial readout.

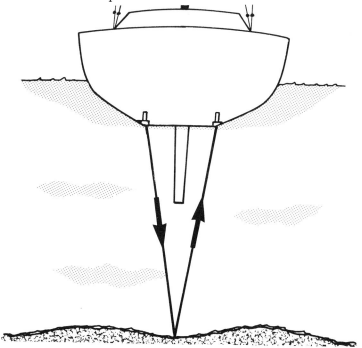

The way in which the sound pulse from an echo sounder is reflected from the sea bed. Two transducers are shown here for clarity but in practice the same transducer is used for both transmission and reception.

The simple description hides the fact that there are a great many variables in echo sounder design which can affect the reading and the use to which it can be put. Understanding the capabilities of the echo sounder will enable the navigator to get the best from it.

From the description of the principles it will be obvious that the echo sounder has to be set for a particular speed of sound in water. Normally the speed used is 4,800 feet per second, but in practice it usually exceed this. This low figure is chosen because it errs on the side of safety. The depths shown will almost invariably be slightly less than actually exists so that the navigator will not be caught out. Where the sounder is used in depths up to 100 feet, the depth is unlikely to underread by more than 5 feet, and in shallow water the error will be very small. The speed of sound in water varies with salinity and temperature and is only likely to approach the 4,800 feet per second mark in fresh water or when the water is very cold. If your boat berths in a river you could be getting more accurate readings as you get into fresh water.

One factor which will affect the performance of your echo sounder is the frequency at which the sound pulse is transmitted. The frequencies in general use are outside the audible range, and vary according to the use for which the sounder is intended. The higher frequencies are better for shallow water use and give a more positive reading even when the bottom is soft mud. With these higher frequencies the range is limited, unless very high powers are used.

The lower frequencies down to 30kHz give much better

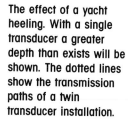

The effect of a yacht heeling. With a single transducer a greater depth than exists will be shown. The dotted lines show the transmission paths of a twin transducer installation.

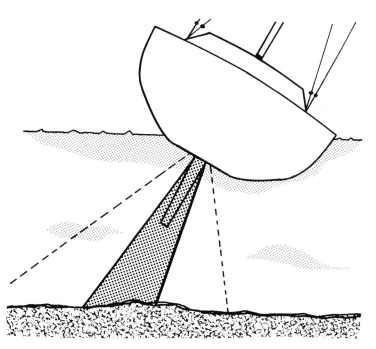

penetration and can work in greater depths with less power, but for these lower frequencies the transducer has to be much larger. A compromise has to be reached and in general small craft echo sounders will work at the higher frequencies, around 150kHz, and for special shallow water sounders the frequencies may be even higher.

At 150kHz the range of a low-powered transducer will not normally exceed 200 feet, but this can be adequate for most small boat navigation. The higher frequency makes the sounder more sensitive to small objects and, if the requirement is to use the sounder to locate shoals of fish as well as to indicate depth, these higher frequencies are better.

Another thing which will reduce the effective range of the sounder is the beam width of the transmitted signal. It is almost impossible to transmit the sound signal as a pencil beam unless a very large reflector is used in the transducer. Physical size prohibits this, so in practice the sound signal is transmitted in the form of a cone. The angle which this cone forms can have quite a bearing on how the set operates.

For deep water work, the cone should be as narrow as possible to concentrate the available power and allow it to penetrate. This would work well if the vessel to which it was fixed were stable, but unfortunately it rolls and pitches in a seaway which would cause a narrow beam to give varying and misleading readings. Deep water sounders usually operate with a beam width of about 15 degrees which is a good compromise, but shallow water sounders extend this to around 50 degrees.

A beam width of 50 degrees allows the transducer to be compact and makes for easy installation, many modern transducers of this type being only two or three inches across. The wide beam width means that soundings are always obtained from the area immediately under the vessel even when it rolls to 25 degrees but the sound energy is dissipated over a wide area thus reducing the effective range of the set. The wide beam-angle can introduce errors into the readings by picking up reflections from shallower areas close by, but these almost invariably err on the safe side.

It is a good idea to find out the following information about your echo sounder, or to ask about it if you are buying one. It can be a good guide to the expected performance.

1. Frequency — a high frequency around 150kHz is usual for shallow water use and gives good discrimination.
2. Beam Width — a wide angle will allow for rolling but reduces the penetration.
3. Power — a power output from the transducer of around 30 watts is normal for a small set. Higher powers will give better penetration.

The various options available with a modern echo sounder installation. The changeover switch can be manual or gravity operated to allow for the downward transducer to be brought into use when a yacht heels over.

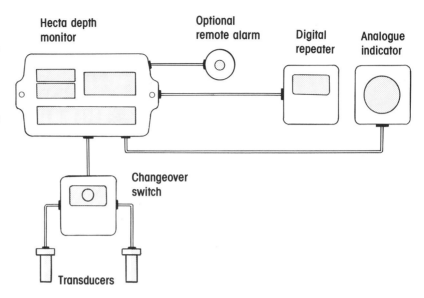

The pulse rate, that is the number of sound pulses transmitted in a second, will vary considerably; anywhere between 5 and 20 is normal for small boat sounders. The higher rates can put more strain on the mechanism but the pulse rate may be varied according to the depth at which the sounder is operating. There must be time for the sound from one pulse to be reflected back to the transducer before the next pulse is transmitted. The receiver is automatically suppressed while the instrument is transmitting, to avoid swamping it with power.

Obviously echoes can be received by the transducer at any time when it is not actually transmitting, and echoes returning from deeper water will sometimes show up on the trace the second time round, giving a false reading. This is often apparent on sounders which are designed to read in both feet and fathoms. In this case, it is a simple matter to switch to the fathoms scale to spot the error. On sounders with only one scale the only way to check is to find out the expected depth from the chart, although this is admittedly not always possible. Once again, the error is on the right side, showing a shallower depth than actually exists, but this can lead to false conclusions.

Presentation

The type of presentation of the information which the echo sounder offers varies between different models and can affect the information which can be obtained. One of the most popular types, largely because it is also the cheapest, is that which indicates the depths by means of a flashing light on a circular scale. Earlier models used a neon flashing light, but this is being replaced by a light emitting diode (LED) in later models. The LED gives a more sensitive reading and at the same time is easier to read in daylight as it is bright red instead of the paler orange of the neon.

This type of presentation shows all the returned echoes above a certain level of gain which are received by the transducer and amplified by the receiver. The strongest of these apart from the transmission signal, indicates the bottom. Any indications between this mark and the transmission mark are usually the result of spurious noise picked up by the transducer or random signals from the amplifier if this is of the cheap type. Some manufacturers boast that echoes returned from fish can be detected by this type of sounder, and there is no doubt that fish do return an echo, but whether the echo could be identified as such is another matter. On a very good quality set, it might be possible, but 'noise' or interference is a much more likely explanation of echoes in the mid-range.

A strong, sharp bottom echo is usually indicative of a hard sea bottom, whereas a soft-edged echo indicates a softer bottom such as mud. Again the quality of the set will determine just how much reliance can be placed on this information. In shallower water, a hard bottom will often produce a double echo, where the sound pulse has travelled to the bottom, been reflected to the boat, reflected down to the bottom again and so back to the transducer. This will show on the screen as a second strong echo at just less than double the depth of the first.

Generally if the flasher type of indicator is giving an unreliable reading, this will be indicated by the vagueness of the flash on the dial. The firmer and more positive the reading, the more reliable it is. This sort of presentation is logical, which is far from the case with those echo sounders which give the readout presented either in digital form or as a pointer on a dial.

The digital display can only show one reading at a time and the circuits are designed to pick out the strongest echo and indicate this. There is little indication of how reliable the reading is and obviously the type of bottom cannot be determined, but a rapidly changing number will indicate that the reading should not be trusted.

The same applies to the dial indicator where the depth is indicated on a pointer. This type gives a slightly better indication of unreliability as the pointer will waver if it is not sure. One thing to be said for both of these types is that they both read low if the reading is unreliable, so that at least they err on the side of safety.

From the navigator's point of view the paper recorder type of echo sounder is by far and away the best. Not only does it indicate the acutal depth in a manner which can be interpreted easily, but it also shows the trend: whether the water is getting deeper or shallower, or whether the vessel has passed over a ridge or a trough. This information can be of great value, often much more so than the actual depth itself.

The recording type of echo sounder is obviously more expensive and complicated than the other types, and it costs more to run as the paper has to be paid for. Some models combine both the paper and flasher types in one model, so that the recording facility need only be used when required. This type is very good and can give the navigator all the information he requires.

With modern electronics the paper display can be replaced by a video screen. This shows the bottom contours in the same way as the paper and the display can be frozen for close examination to identify fish or other details. Some models have a memory for storage, but this is getting into the realms of expensive sonar equipment not normally carried on board yachts. These video displays can be in monochrome or colour and by using colour it is possible for the weaker and stronger returns to be separated. These colour systems are largely used for fish finding and are generally too expensive to be justified for general navigation use.

Another recent innovation is the speaking echo sounder which can be a useful way of presentation if you do a lot of navigating in shallow water. It allows you to concentrate on other aspects of navigation whilst keeping one ear cocked for the soundings, but you have to have considerable faith in electronics to rely on the electronic voice.

Accuracy and Calibration

We have already seen how the accuracy of the echo sounder is dependant on the density and temperature of the water. These are variable errors which you can do little about unless you want highly accurate readings. But you will want to check the accuracy of the echo sounder occasionally just to make sure you can rely on it. This can be done in the marina by comparing the indicated depth with the depth measured by a pole. This should be done on a hard bottom because the readings can be distorted on a very soft bottom. The difference between the two readings is likely to be the distance from the water surface to the transducer surface but you must bear in mind, when using the echo sounder to close limits, that the keel may be below the transducer. You may have to deduct several feet of the sounder reading to get the depth under the keel.

On some sounders it is possible to adjust the depth setting so that the sounder can show the under-keel clearance or the depth from the surface. Whichever setting you choose it is wise to put a note by the sounder because there can be a considerable difference between the two. The depth under the keel is probably the best reading to set for shallow water navigation.

The accuracy of the echo sounder can be checked in deeper water by a comparison with a lead-line reading. Be careful if you make any adjustment to this reading because it may alter the shallow water reading, and you want that to be as accurate as possible.

Logs

From the traditional towed impeller type of log, log design has developed rapidly under the influence of modern electronics. Most logs measure the speed of the boat through the water which is fine when you are assessing performance, but is only of limited use for navigation where speed over the ground is more important as a measure of progress. Doppler logs which relate the change in frequency of a reflected sound signal from the sea bed to the speed of the vessel, do indicate the speed over the ground directly, but tend to be expensive and are rarely used on yachts. With modern position finding equipment, the speed over the ground can be obtained from successive positions of the yacht and logs today are mainly used for performance assessment, but they do have an important role still in dead reckoning and for the speed input required for Transit satellite navigation receivers.

Types of Log

There are several different types of modern electronic log as distinct from the traditional towed log. The different types have different characteristics which can affect their accuracy so that it is as well to know how you can expect your log to behave. The towed log still has its place and there are navigators who prefer it because it is easy to haul in the rotator and check it or substitute it, if there is a discrepancy in the readings. Modern versions, as with electronic types, present the information on a dial in the wheelhouse or cockpit but they are not as convenient as hull-mounted logs. You have to remember to take the rotator and line in before you stop or enter harbour.

The most common type of log now used substitutes a small impeller mounted under the hull, in place of the rotator towed astern. Whereas the rotator has to operate a mechanical drive which will cause some slip in the rotator, this impeller transmits its information electro-magnetically. A small magnet is embedded in the hub and this creates a pulse on each rotation. Counting these

In the paddle wheel log impeller, pulses from the embedded magnets are picked up by the sensor and counted to give speed.

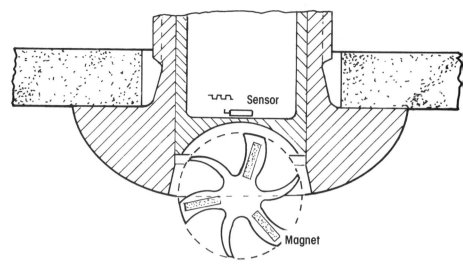

pulses gives the distance travelled and, from this, the speed.

If both the rotator and the impeller are to work accurately, they should be in clear water. This is not too difficult with the rotator which is towed astern in relatively undisturbed water, but the line must be long enough to keep the rotator clear of the propeller wash and deep enough to be away from any surface effect. The impeller, being close to the hull, will be affected by any uneven flow around the hull, and it will have to be carefully sited if the readings are to be meaningful. In both these types the rotator or impeller has a certain inertia which has to be overcome, and this can make readings at very slow speeds unreliable. This is particularly the case with the towed type, where readings below three knots may be suspect. Impeller-type readings will normally be reasonably accurate down to one or two knots, which should cover most practical purposes.

Anything turning in the water is liable to be fouled by the debris which seems to abound in the sea these days. Weed is probably the greatest hazard and most logs of the impeller type have a weed deflector, which is simply an angled plate fitted in front of the impeller. This certainly helps by not giving the weed anything vital on which to catch, but these fittings are also prone to damage by pieces of floating debris which are deflected under the hull.

It is often possible to withdraw the impeller at sea either to clear it or to repair it. This type of retractable fitting will also avoid damage when the boat is being lifted out of the water or slipped. Fixed impellers which cannot be withdrawn are cheaper, but it means slipping the boat if the impeller gets damaged.

A very similar type of log measures the pressure of the water due to the forward motion of the boat. A small open-ended tube projects into the water flow in much the same way as the impeller, and the pressure is a direct indication of the speed of the boat. It has the advantage of simplicity, but the projecting tube is prone to blockage or damage as obviously it cannot be protected like the impeller. This log is generally reserved for high speed craft and mounted on the bottom of the transom.

Another type is the electromagnetic log, which uses a familiar electrical principle to measure speed. If a conductor of electricity (in this case water) is moving in a magnetic field, it will have an electrical current induced in it. In practice, the transducer consists of two small electrodes to pick up the induced current, which is then measured directly on a scale, giving the speed.

The advantage is that there are virtually no projections from the hull, the transducer being almost flush. The readings are still valid down to very low speeds and there is little chance of damage from floating debris. The readings do depend on a good flow of water past the transducer face, which is fine when the boat is clean, but a dirty bottom can considerably upset the flow of water close to the hull and this will make the log read low. Marine growth can also attach itself to the transducer face which must not be covered with antifouling paint. For this reason the transducer is often made capable of being withdrawn for cleaning.

Because the transducer is so close to the hull surface, it has to be positioned carefully to make sure that there is a good flow of water. On displacement hulls this would normally be near amidships but well clear of, and preferably forward of any projections such as bilge keels, water intake and echo sounder transducers. On planing boats, the forward part of the hull is often clear of the water so a position well aft should be chosen, but again well clear of shafts and other projections.

The Doppler log is used to measure speed through the water. For this purpose a weak signal is adequate, reducing the cost and complexity of the equipment. The signal is reflected back from particles in the water to give an accurate speed reading, but in very shallow water, bottom-reflected signals may give confusing readings.

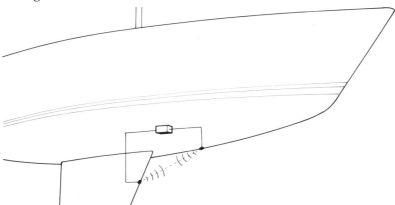

The 'sonic speed' log measures the speed of sound between two underwater transducers. The speed is increased by the speed of the yacht and this system gives highly accurate speed readings with minimum interference.

Yet one more type of log also uses transmitted sound signals, but these are passed between two transducers on the hull. These transducers are mounted on the fore-and-aft line, one on the keel and one on the hull surface forward. The time it takes for the signal to pass from one transducer to the other will be directly affected by the speed of the water it passes through and this is used to indicate the speed. This log is not prone to damage and is very sensitive to speed variation, working reliably at very low speeds. It is primarily intended for fitting to sailing yacht hulls as the required locations for the transducers would not normally be available on a powerboat hull.

Most electronic logs are accurate to about two per cent at best. This means that on a 100 mile run the reading could be two miles out either way giving a four mile wide band in which the boat may lie. This two per cent accuracy can only be obtained after the log has been calibrated. Calibration involves running the boat over a measured distance, usually a mile, in each direction and from this working out the boat's speed. The two-way runs substantially cancel out the effects of wind and tide, but a reasonably calm day should be chosen just the same. A comparison of the actual speed and the recorded speed will show the error, and most logs are fitted with an adjustment to eliminate or at least reduce the error of the readings.

After adjustment, further runs over the measured distance should be made to check the reading. If all is well, the log can then be assumed to be reasonably accurate for that particular speed. Runs can be made at other throttle settings and it will usually be found that the errors will vary according to the speed. This has to be accepted and if necessary, the error can be applied to the log readings. The log is usually calibrated to give maximum accuracy at the normal cruising speed.

Log readings will usually show increased errors in rough seas, due to the more erratic movement of the water past the impeller and to aeration of the water under the hull. The readings will often be on the high side, but this is by no means certain and a great deal will depend on the prevailing conditions.

From all this it will be obvious that log readings, both of the speed and the distance, must be treated with a great deal of caution when they are used for navigation. Under sail there is no alternative way to measuring speed through the water but under power, the engine rpm can give a good guide. If runs over the measured mile are done at different engine rpm then it is possible to relate the rpm directly to speed, although head or tail winds may make a considerable difference and head seas usually require more rpm to maintain speed.

On a sailing yacht one of the most valuable uses of a log is to

Matching log and echo sounder unit showing the transducers. The log has the option of a towed impeller or a through-hull paddle wheel.

Log and echo sounder dials using large format LCD displays. These allow both analogue and digital readouts to be shown on the same display.

check performance. It is not so much the absolute speed that is of interest, but the relative speed which can measure the affect of sail changes and trimming. Special logs have been developed for this purpose where the scale can be expanded over a section of the speed range and this gives a very sensitive relative speed readout. The same type of relative measurement of speed could be used on a powerboat. When related to engine rpm it could show up any deterioration in performance caused through hull fouling or other causes. These applications will be looked at further in the next chapter.

The basic type of echo sounder with a circular scale on which the depth is indicated by a flashing light.

Compasses

Compasses are included in this book because the electronic compass is being used more and more in yachts. The magnetic compass is well known and well understood and the electronic compass, or to give it its proper name the fluxgate compass, still uses the earth's magnetic field as its heading reference, but instead of the swinging compass needle or card, the direction is sensed

electronically to give a readout compatible with modern electronic navigation systems.

The fluxgate is a special type of coil which can sense the direction of the earth's magnetic field. It is rather like the coils in an RDF loop and the fluxgate compass can operate with either a single rotating coil or with two fixed coils at right angles to each other in the same way as an RDF antenna.

The rotating coil type has had only limited application for fluxgate compasses. With this type, the navigator has to set the course he wants to steer on a 360 degree dial and then the compass indicator simply shows whether the course being steered is to the left or right of the required course. The helmsman has no numbers to read and a quick glance will indicate which way to turn the wheel, making this type of presentation very logical and particularly well suited to high performance sail or power craft.

Tradition, however, plays an important role and it appears that most helmsmen prefer a traditional compass display. This is where the twin-coil fluxgate comes in because it can be linked to a rotating compass card or a rotating needle on a fixed card. Either way the full 360 degrees are displayed in the more familiar type of compass display. Another option with the twin-coil fluxgate is to use a digital compass readout, which is fine for information purposes, but not suitable for steering a course by.

Because the information produced by the fluxgate compass is in electronic form it can be processed by a micro-processor to suit the requirements. Damping can be introduced to allow the card to have a nice steady reading with none of the wild swings normally associated with a magnetic compass in a rough sea. Fluxgate compasses still need correcting in the same way as magnetic compasses because they are affected by the magnetic influence of

A fluxgate compass with the sensor contained in the heading reference box and the analogue display designed for panel mounting.

the vessel, but both variation and deviation corrections can be applied electronically so that the compass can give a true reading if required.

Some fluxgate compasses coming on to the market are self-correcting. By switching to a calibrate mode and swinging the vessel through 360 degrees the deviation is automatically calibrated and then applied to the compass readings. This allows the compass to be calibrated quickly and easily before each passage and saves the expense of the compass adjuster, although the initial cost of the units is higher.

Perhaps the biggest attraction of the fluxgate compass is its compatibility with other electronic equipment. It can provide the essential heading input for satellite navigation receivers, auto-pilots and sailing and navigation computers. The indicator dials can be mounted in any convenient location and at any angle and they are not affected by magnetic influence so that they can be in a wheelhouse full of electronics without problems. The master unit can be located in a position away from magnetic influence to give the best readings.

Not to be outdone by the fluxgate compass, the standard magnetic compass is also undergoing a revolution. Many compasses of this type are now fitted with pick-up coils which convert the compass information into electronic signals which can be used in much the same way as that from fluxgate compasses. However all compasses may become a thing of the past except for emergency use because modern position finding equipment is becoming sensitive enough to detect deviations from a set course and to provide instructions to the autopilot to bring the vessel back on course. This can be done without any heading reference and simply uses the displacement of the vessel to one side or the other of the desired track. Most navigators will want to retain a compass as a back-up and in this respect it should be remembered that the fluxgate compass needs a power supply so there is still a place for the standard magnetic compass which is self-sustaining.

Autopilots

From the section on compasses it becomes clear that an autopilot system is becoming an essential link between modern electronic navigation equipment and the host vessel. Whilst a human helmsman needs a compass reference to steer by in order to maintain a set course, modern autopilots can obtain steering information from position finding systems which will maintain the vessel on the desired track rather than the course, something the human helmsman would find much harder to do. This can lead to much more accurate navigation with the effects of tide, currents, wind and helmsman's bias being taken into account automatically.

Autopilots can receive steering information from three sources. Position finding equipment can provide information to maintain the vessel on a desired track, whilst a compass can provide a reference to keep the vessel on a desired course. The third reference applies to sailing vessels and is a wind reference which will keep the vessel sailing on at a constant angle to the wind. This latter system is used primarily when close hauled, to keep the yacht at the best angle to the wind, but can also be used when running to prevent the yacht gybing. The ability of an autopilot to accept different references should be considered carefully when selecting a unit, and the wind reference might be useful on a powerboat in heavy weather although manual steering would

A fully fledged autopilot system showing the various components which can be incorporated. A simple yacht system may miss out some of these components in the interests of economy.

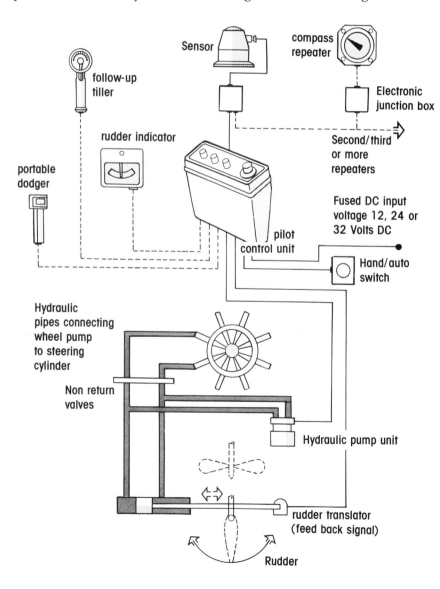

follow-up tiller

Sensor

compass repeater

Electronic junction box

Second/third or more repeaters

rudder indicator

portable dodger

pilot control unit

Fused DC input voltage 12, 24 or 32 Volts DC

Hand/auto switch

Hydraulic pipes connecting wheel pump to steering cylinder

Non return valves

Hydraulic pump unit

rudder translator (feed back signal)

Rudder

probably be a safer approach.

The modern autopilot is a micro-processor controlled unit which can match the steering of the vessel to the prevailing conditions. Controls are usually incorporated to limit the rudder angle, the amount of swing before corrective action is applied and damping to allow for compass swing in rough seas. The adaptive autopilot is even more sophisticated because it senses the steering characteristics of the vessel in relation to the sea and wind conditions and almost anticipates the swing of the vessel so that corrective action can be be applied. The result is a steering action which maintains the vessel on course accurately with improved fuel economy and reduced wear and tear on the steering gear. This type of autopilot can also reduce the power requirements for steering which can be an important feature on sailing yachts.

The power systems for autopilots can be electric or hydraulic. The former is normal for yacht use. Electrically powered systems for wheel steering have an electric motor connected to the steering system with a chain or belt drive which can be clutched in or out. This is a form of power steering and most autopilots allow manual control of this power steering, often with a small control panel on an electric lead to give a form of remote control.

An alternative autopilot system is designed for tiller steering which operates electrically in a push-pull fashion. The principle is much the same as for wheel steering autopilots except for the acutal drive mechanism. These tiller units are fully self-contained and make installation simple. Comparable types of self-contained autopilot for wheel steering are also available as bolt-on units designed for smaller craft. These units tend to lack the refinements of the larger units, but are generally adequate for most small craft steering requirements.

The inclusion of a micro-processor in the autopilot control often leaves processing capacity available for other functions. A navigation computer is sometimes incorporated which duplicates that already available in the position finding system. This is one of the penalties paid for buying equipment as individual units and in the future we are likely to see autopilot systems much more closely linked to position finding equipment as part of an integrated package.

A tiller steering auto-pilot with integral compass unit. The yoke is fixed to the cockpit and the extension arm links to the tiller.

6 Wind and weather displayed

A range of wind instruments with the masthead sensor unit. Without a compass input, the wind direction is only the apparent wind.

Sailing instruments are becoming a feature of sail boats as demonstrated by the rows of dials now commonly seen in the cockpits of yachts. To a certain extent they are replacing the 'seat of the pants' type of sailing expertise by quantifying many of the wind and weather factors which affect a sailing yacht. Whilst these instruments can be a great help to more efficient sailing, the information they present must be balanced against experience for the best results. These instruments can help the inexperienced a great deal to sharpen the process of learning to sail efficiently by showing the effects of sail trimming.

The use of electronics for improving sailing efficiency is a rapidly developing area as manufacturers seek to harness new ways of measuring the parameters involved and new ways of processing the information to make it meaningful and useful. This is an obvious area where computers can help and the development of complex computerised systems is likely to increase.

Wind Speed and Direction

The measurement of wind speed and direction are made at the masthead where the wind flow is least disturbed. Here the wind sensors are competing with other antennae such as the VHF antenna and the wind sensors are usually mounted on an arm cantilevered out from the mast to allow them to work in clear air.

The direction sensor is a simple weather vane embodying an electromagnetic sensor system. The three armed rotating caps of the wind speed sensor are a familiar sight and again electro-magnetic sensing is normally used to count the rotations which are then translated electronically into wind speed on the dial.

The display for both of these instruments can be either analogue or digital. For wind direction an analogue dial is preferred because it is a more logical display and the wind speed is usually shown on a matching analogue dial, but may also be incorporated on the direction dial as a digital readout. The type of display is largely a matter of personal choice bearing in mind that these two instruments indicate only the apparent speed and direction of the wind, and that this information on its own is not of vital importance.

Apparent wind speed has a role to play in sailing efficiency and dictates the angle at which a yacht can sail to the wind close hauled and also the gybing point when the wind is aft. Much more important in many respects is the true wind speed and direction but this cannot be measured directly unless the yacht is stationary. It can be obtained indirectly by applying the yacht's course and speed to the apparent wind speed and direction and, although complex in terms of trigonometry, such a calculation is simple for the modern micro-processor and is only the starting point for a range of calculations which are possible from the raw information. Some of this raw information comes from sensors and some from human estimation. The complexity of the instrumentation and hence the cost is largely a question of how much the human input is replaced by sensor information.

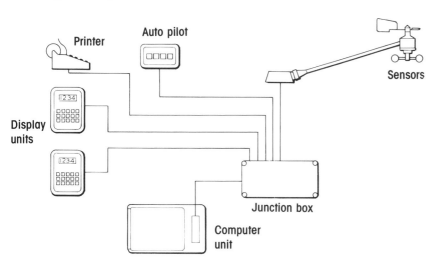

Printer

Auto pilot

Sensors

Display units

Junction box

Computer unit

The basic units of an integrated system. The sensors can include log, wind speed and direction, depth, position finding systems and time outputs can be in both analogue and digital form as well as connecting to printers, autopilots and satnavs.

One of the most important factors for efficient sailing is the velocity made good (VMG). Most yachtsmen know that if you sail a yacht too close to the wind it appears to be making good progress to windward because of the course being steered, but in fact progress to windward is slower because of reduced boat speed. The opposite is true if you sail too far off the wind because, whereas the boat speed rises, the direction taken is less advantageous. Somewhere between these two is the optimum combination of boat speed and direction and one of the most important dials of the sailing efficiency system is that denoting VMG.

This figure is obtained by noting the true wind direction and then using course and speed combination for the yacht to show how much progress is being made in that direction. To this apparently simple calculation ought to be added inputs for leeway and tidal current and these can be inserted manually. Where an electronic position finding system is available, such as Loran C or a Decca Navigator, this position information gives a better picture of the progress being made, because the measurements are made 'over the ground' rather than 'through the water' and the former is the most relevant in terms of making progress towards a fixed point.

Even without the position finding input, these integrated systems can develop much useful information. Whilst the leeway and tidal corrections will have to be assessed manually, the helmsman's bias can at least be identified and corrected. Most helmsmen will tend to steer to one side of a course rather than the other. This will set the yacht away from the desired track. The continuously updated DR positions obtained from the course and speed inputs will identify this bias as a cross-track error to the left or right.

There is a wide variety of ways in which the information from these sailing instruments can be presented. The growing rank of dials in yacht cockpits is testimony to this fact, and this has led to a search for alternative means of presentation. The analogue dials commonly used are good insofar as they separate out the information, but the layout and similarity of the dials can cause confusion. The important information is not readily identifiable. The separation and layout of the dials can help, but one alternative is a digital display. Many yachtsmen, however, find a digital display harder to interpret and certainly it has less 'feeling' than an analogue display.

A more recent development is multi-function displays on which a number of parameters can be selected by simply punching the appropriate buttons. This type of display assumes that you will only want one of the parameters at any one time and the switching operation between one and the other can be a nuisance. In practice a combination of analogue and digital displays provides the optimum solution, but the arrangement has to be carefully thought out in relation to the use of the information.

Heading information is vital to course steering whilst VMG is important if you wish to make rapid progress to windward. In other directions the speed variation can be critical to keeping the yacht sailing at its optimum speed rather than the absolute speed through the water.

With the advent of larger LCD types of display it is possible to concentrate a lot more information into a single display. The use of graphical types of display can make interpretation easier and more logical and it is possible to get the whole range of sailing efficiency, wind and course information on to one display. Even here it is possible for confusion to arise in a quick glance at the display, but practice helps to identify the salient features. This type of graphical display is likely to become more commonplace particularly where a large amount of information has to be presented in an easy to assimilate fashion. These LCD displays can be made waterproof allowing them to be installed in the cockpit. Because of the wide range of information displayed the control knob can be left down below.

Computer Based Systems

These sailing efficiency systems only take into account the broad parameters which affect the performance of a sailing yacht. A much more complex assessment is possible taking into account a wide variety of parameters, all of which affect sailing performance. These complex systems are already on the market having first been developed for 12 metre racing yachts and are now finding their way on board top ocean-racing yachts. They are based on standard computers with specially written software programmes and the large screen VDU display makes possible the use of graphics to display the complex information.

To a certain extent the software programmes used on these systems are adaptive, in as much as they assess the information about the performance of the yacht under different conditions and thus build up a data base. From an analysis of this data base it is possible to identify the best sailing performance of a yacht under particular wind and sea conditions and to optimise the performance.

These computer based systems have a wide variety of sensors to provide the raw information. In addition to the standard wind, course, speed and position information they will measure the condition of the boat. Inputs will cover fore-and-aft trim, angle of heel, weight distribution, rigging tension and sails. Some of these inputs may be manual, but the computer will assess all the different factors which can affect the performance. As the data bank is built up it will be able to indicate the optimum condition of the yacht to suit the ambient wind and sea conditions and the course required. As racing yachts experiment more with variable geometry in hulls and keels the type of computer system will become essential to produce the best combination for the particular conditions.

Whilst equipment such as this has an obvious place on top racing yachts, it can also be useful in assessing the performance of production yachts. The day will soon come when yacht builders will carry out a full computer assessment of the sailing performance of a standard production yacht so that the customer can have the benefit of the analysis to help him sail the yacht more efficiently.

A new approach to sailing efficiency currently being developed is to replace the parameter of wind and speed with pressure. This is being done because the affect of the wind on the sails of a yacht is less affected by the speed of the air, but by the pressure they exert. This pressure determines the angle of the heel, the leeway and the stress on the sails as well as the efficiency of converting the wind into sailing effort. By using pressure as the means of assessing the wind, the effect of the wind can be more accurately measured and forecast.

The use of a compass input allows the important VMG to be calculated. The two top dials in this display are multi-function instruments which allow a number of parameters to be displayed but only one can be displayed at a time.

A computer based system which can generate polar diagrams showing anticipated sailing performance under the prevailing conditions. This system uses temperature as well as wind strength to calculate the wind effect on the sails.

The pressure exerted by the wind varies not just with the wind speed, but also with the temperatures. Wind pressure is affected by the weight or density of the air and this is directly related to the temperature; warm air being less dense than cold air. By adding temperature sensors to the list of parameters fed into the computer it is claimed that a more accurate assessment of the performance can be made in the light of the ambient conditions.

Recognising that the measurements of performance need a yardstick against which they can be judged, some of the computer programmes incorporate the performance of a perfect yacht of the same type as the host vessel. This figure then acts as a yardstick or target, showing the performance which ought to be possible in the given conditions. A display shows the percentage efficiency obtained against this target figure. This can be useful in the tuning process of a racing yacht.

Taken to extremes, these computer based sailing instruments can dictate the sailing programme. They can be programmed to show the optimum combination of sails for the ambient conditions, the optimum course to steer and the way the yacht should be trimmed. Whilst the cruising yachtsman will probably shy rapidly away from such automation, the racing yachtsman seems to be intent on following this path. The advantage is that the computer does not rest, but is always trying to optimise the performance. Given the right programme with the right balance of the many different factors it should be more efficient than the average human skipper. A redeeming feature perhaps of these computer systems at present is that they still require a considerable human input to operate efficiently.

With refinement these computer systems may overtake the human element which could spell the end of competitive sailing as we know it. Whilst the computers themselves, however, are very efficient, the transducers which supply the information to the computer are less efficient and accurate. Whilst the information processed by the computer has the appearance of being highly accurate, it must be remembered that it will only be as good as the raw information fed into it. This is the case with all of these sailing efficiency instruments and there is still quite a long way to go down the path of development.

7 Charts by electronics

The video display unit (VDU) and its ability to show graphics has provided the basis by which charts are moving into the electronic era. Already plotters which allow a vessel's position and track to be displayed against a position grid are in wide use and the addition of the detailed chart information is only a short step forward for these plotters. This forward step, however, is fraught with both technical and political problems and it is likely to be quite a while before electronic charts become widespread on board yachts.

Whilst plotters and electronic charts are a logical development along the path of fully integrated navigation and computer control systems, they do not offer any great advantage for yachts in their present form. They are bulky pieces of equipment to find space for, and they are expensive. As far as electronic equipment is concerned both plotters and electronic charts must presently be a long way down the list of priorities as far as yachts are concerned, but developments in electronics are so rapid that this position may not last. Certainly electronic charts are hard to justify economically as a replacement for paper charts, but in the long term, the electronic chart could develop as the optimum display for integrated navigation systems. As some of the systems available are aimed at the yacht market they have a place in this book.

Plotters

The plotters used for navigation show the position of the vessel in relation to a grid. This grid can be either latitude or longitude usually on the Mercator projection or it can relate to the position lines generated by one of the hyperbolic navigation systems. With a plotter, the vessel's track is displayed, both the present position and the historical positions and this type of display is often used for fishing or survey work but is rarely relevant for general navigation. As plotters, however, form the basis of many electronic chart systems they demand a closer look.

There are two main types of plotter. The older type uses a paper sheet or roll with a mechanical pen. The pen moves across the paper under the guidance of an electronic position finding system and draws the track of the vessel, the pen indicating the present position. The benefit of this system is that it offers a permanent record of the track for future reference. When a paper roll is used the movement of the paper creates the Y-axis movements and the

A paper based plotter which allows a permanent course record to be maintained but which lacks the flexibility of electronic plotters.

pen the X-axis.

The alternative is a fully electronic system using a video screen as the plot. Using this screen the grid lines are generated electronically and the track is shown moving across the screen. With this type of plotter the information on the screen can be stored in the memory or on tape or disk, but the big advantage is the ease with which other information can be displayed.

Most of these electronic plotters have a coastline generator incorporated. By defining points on the screen in terms of latitude and longitude it is possible to draw a basic chart on the screen using selected positions from the coastline so that the vessel's track can then be related to the land or channel edges. This information can be stored in the memory and called up as required. For a vessel using a particular area frequently, a set of coastline or channel charts can be developed in this way, although the number of defined points may be fairly limited and the charted information is consequently also limited. This type of chart generated on the plotter may be of considerable use to the sports fisherman who wants to pinpoint wrecks and other underwater features so that he can find them again using the good repeatability accuracy or Loran or Decca.

With such a system, however, we have the basis of the electronic chart. It can be seen that with a full chart display, a vast amount of information has to be displayed on the screen and this calls for a different plotting approach, but the basic principle is the same.

Electronic Charts

The first types of electronic chart could rightly be described as the plotting table, which is akin to the paper plotter. The plotting table uses a standard chart laid out on the table with a moving carriage below linked to a position finding system. The position of the vessel is indicated on the chart by means of a pinpoint of light shining upwards. These plotting tables occupy a great deal of space and are not suitable for yachts.

This concept, however, has been refined by photographing the charts on to small transparencies. These are carried on a moving frame the position of which is controlled by the position finding system. The transparency carriage is mounted in a projector so that the chart shines on to a translucent screen, with the vessel's position shown at the centre of the screen. Such a system is reasonably compact and the saving in chart storage space compensates for the space required for the equipment. Being a mechanical system, it will never quite achieve the reliability possible with modern electronics. Such a system does, however, represent one of the alternative chart systems suitable for larger yachts pending the development of cheaper fully electronic systems. This is a US system and charts for most US coastal waters are available.

The fully electronic chart uses the video screen for the display. Because of the large amount of information required to be displayed on a small screen, a high resolution is required, certainly considerably better than the average TV screen. This raises the cost and is one of the reasons why only small screen displays are used with the electronic chart systems available so far. Another reason of course is the larger space required but even big ship systems still use the smaller screens because of the cost of high resolution video tubes. Colour displays with the necessary resolution are even more expensive, although the use of colour can make it easier to interpret congested information. As tube technology develops the use of colour displays will become the norm for electronic charts.

For electronic charts, the chart information is first digitised and then stored on a cartridge or disk depending on the memory system in use. Once stored in the memory in this way, the user can call up the particular chart he requires from a menu selection. Most systems use charts taken directly from the standard catalogue so that the menu will contain a familiar selection. Because of the small size of the display it is rare that the chart will be used in its entirety but one of the big advantages of the electronic chart is the flexibility of the display method. This allows the specific area of interest to be displayed.

Electronic chart systems differ in the way charts are used. Some systems only allow the chart to be displayed at the appropriate scale of the chart in storage so that charts are stored on different scales depending on the level of interest. The amount of detail available relates to the scale of the chart with harbour areas having a wealth of detail and open sea areas much less. Such a display system is easy to produce from existing charts, but the trend is towards a much more flexible system which allows the user to have the chart presented on the screen at any scale which is appropriate to the use.

This allows the user to zoom in on particular areas of interest or have the chart presented on a small scale for voyage planning. It may be possible to vary the scale in steps or for it to be infinitely variable, it is simply a matter of giving the appropriate commands to the electronics.

The flexibility of the electronic chart can lead to false assumptions being made and care has to be taken in their use. The ability to expand the chart to a large scale may mean that there is a temptation to navigate to close limits, but it must be remembered that the information on which the chart is based may not justify this level of accuracy. Many charts were produced when position finding did not have the present-day level of accuracy, and of course the sea bed and other navigation features may change. Keeping charts up-to-date is a constant challenge and it is easy to forget this with the electronic chart presentation and use it to an accuracy beyond that for which it was designed.

When using an electronic chart on a large scale, there is usually adequate room for the presentation of detailed information. On smaller scales, however, congestion can quickly build up. A paper chart contains a wealth of detailed information and it is a constant challenge to present this clearly and unambiguously. The use of colour can help, but the electronic chart has to present this same information on a monochrome screen which has a much poorer resolution than the paper chart. Numbers and letters in particular present a problem because they can only be made so small and still remain legible.

The solution found for this is to have the information stored in a series of overlays. The basic page will show the coastline, and then the user can call up some or all of the overlays in order to build up the chart with just the information which is required for the particular task. The type of overlays which are used might comprise bottom contours, bottom characteristics, navigation marks, shore features, traffic routes, wrecks, etc. The amount of information in the data base is considerable and by using this overlay system the user can build up a selective chart. It is rather like having the chart made up from a series of transparent sheets, each with certain information on them. Put all the sheets together and you have the complete chart but with electronic charts these sheets are added or removed electronically.

In addition to this selective chart information, if the chart system is linked to a position finding system, the vessel's track will be shown moving across the screen. It is possible for the vessel to remain in the centre of the screen and for the chart to scroll by, but this requires a powerful computer and the more normal system is for the vessel to track across the screen. Some chart systems allow for the chart display to move forward in steps automatically and it is even possible for the system to switch charts automatically so that the user has a continuously updated display suited to the navigation task.

The switch from a paper chart to an electronic chart will be difficult because it takes time to adjust to the different format. Because the navigator has a choice over the information which is displayed, he will have to be careful that vital information is not left off the screen. The hydrographic authorities are looking carefully at the legal aspects of electronic charts because they introduce new concepts into chart presentation. No longer is the paper chart as printed by the hydrographic authority the direct information link to the navigator, but middleman in the form of chart digitisers and the software programme writers will come into the act, and the question of responsibility and liability have to be considered. This is an area where the technology is leaping ahead of the planning and legislation and is causing the hydrographic authorities some concern.

Despite these problems and the lack of any form of standardisation the electronic chart is progressing. It may take the development of new electronic concepts before these chart systems become practical on smaller yachts, but just as the computer is now available in small portable packages, so the electronic chart will also be developed into small packages. The incentive for this development will probably come after the introduction of the Navstar GPS satellite navigation system which will make car electronic map systems feasible. This much wider market will hasten development of small or flat displays which will fit comfortably into small yachts. The prospects for electronic chart systems in full colour may be a long way off, but they offer the prospect of navigation lights flashing in their appropriate sequence, features which will bring a whole new dimension and realism to chart displays.

Correcting Electronic Charts

Correcting paper charts is a slow laborious business, but one which is very necessary for efficient navigation. One of the big advantages in using electronic charts is the prospect they offer of carrying out corrections automatically. Because the chart is stored electronically, it is very simple to correct or change this information electronically and a number of schemes have been proposed, but introduction of these systems may not be as straightforward as it seems.

Firstly the chart system has to be designned to allow correction. This is easy to design into the system, but protection also has to be provided so that the integrity of the chart data base is maintained. If the data base can be changed at will then the chart information is no longer reliable. The simplest method of correction is for the chart disks or cartridges to be changed at regular intervals. This would probably be adequate for most yacht use, but the system should also be able to embrace more urgent changes received by radio or telex. Some chart systems are being developed which can be upgraded by radio signals through a direct link.

The real problem with correction lies in the lack of standardisation of electronic chart systems. This means that each individual manufacturer has to develop his own correction service which can add considerably to the cost.

The need for standardisation is already apparent, but as more systems come on to the market, the more difficult it becomes to reach agreement on standardisation. The situation is complicated by being an international one and this lack of standardisation may hold back the widespread use of electronic charts.

Integration and Development

Charts represent probably the last of the traditional navigation tools to be converted to electronics. The conversion has been slow to materialise because of the complex electronics involved and also because the initial development does not offer much advancement over existing paper charts. Because the electronic

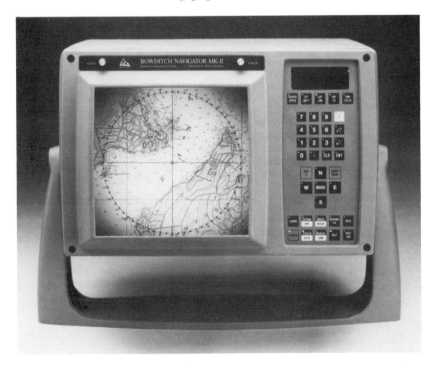

An early electronic chart system where the chart is projected onto a screen, with the movement of the chart controlled by information from a position finding system. The yacht's position remains at the centre of the screen.

chart does not give a permanent record of the vessel's progress on a voyage, the use of an electronic chart can even increase the workload because the paper chart plot has to be maintained alongside the electronic chart to guard against electrical failure and as a permanent record.

Because of this and the difficulties over standardisation, the electronic chart in its present form does not offer any great advantages. Its cost is high and it offers little in the way of better operating economics or efficiency. For yachts in particular it is probably a system which most yachtsmen would happily do without in its present form. In the longer term, however, electronic charts are a logical development because if the whole navigation system is to go electronic, then the essential chart which is the reference for the whole navigation exercise cannot be left out on its own.

Only by having charts in electronic form can they be integrated into the other electronic systems. We have already seen how charts are not simply a display, but a link with position finding systems to provide a full plot. Electronic charts have also been linked to radar and here we come into the realms of the one display system which will meet all navigation requirements. This will be covered more fully in the next chapter, but could provide the incentive for electronic chart development. Compared with other electronic systems, electronic charts are still in their infancy and have a long way to go. An electronic chart display in the cockpit of a yacht may seem like science fiction, but it is practical now and with future electronic development, it will almost certainly become reality.

A portable electronic chart system which has been designed for use by pilots navigating large ships but which could form the basis of a yacht system.

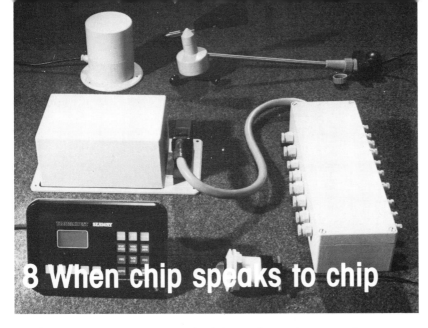

8 When chip speaks to chip

Just some of the components of a fully integrated system. The computer unit is the white box on the middle left linked to the junction box on the right which in turn links up all the transducers and displays.

The computer is a wonderful machine. It can take in raw information, process and refine it and then either store it or present it to the user. It is the ability of the computer to handle vast amounts of information and to carry out highly complex calculations that have revolutionised yacht electronics. Not only has it allowed complex electronic equipment to be fitted into a compact package suitable for yachts, but it has reduced the power demands of the equipment and improved the reliability. Gone are many of the complex mechanical or electro-mechanical instruments to be replaced by securely packaged electronics with no moving parts to wear out.

The computer or micro-processor has been at the heart of this revolution. There is hardly a piece of electronic equipment used on yachts today which does not have a computer of some sort incorporated in it. From the humble log right up to the latest satellite navigation system, the computer is an essential component. In all these instruments, however, the computer is dedicated to the particular task and cannot be used for other functions even if spare capacity is available. Each piece of equipment is a 'stand alone' instrument, which, whilst it may have outlet or inlet ports for linking to other equipment, is primarily designed for autonomous use.

One of the future steps down the electronic path will be to replace many of these dedicated computers with one central computer. Into this computer will be fed the raw information from a wide range of sensors on the yacht. The computer will take this raw information and will process it into information which is of value for navigation or vessel monitoring. The main purpose of following this route is that it allows the information for the wide variety of sources on board to be inter-related to provide useful monitoring, navigation or communications information. For instance the fuel consumption can be related to the speed over the ground, the target shown ahead on the radar can be related to the buoy shown on the chart. Such fully integrated systems are already being developed and although this development is primarily aimed at the shipping market, embryo concepts for yacht use are also under development. The possibilities of such systems are almost limitless, leading towards full automation and remote control and they follow on as a logical development of the use of computers on board yachts.

Hand-held Computers

The small hand-held mathematical computer was one of the first computers to find its way on board yachts. In their simplest form these computers were used for solving the vector triangle and other navigation problems associated with dead reckoning. More sophisticated computers could solve the spherical trigonometry problems associated with taking astronomical sights. From here it was a short step towards specially programmed computers which could handle these sight reductions on a semi-automatic basis, given the basic data such as altitude, declination and other relevant information. The memory capacity of some modern computers of this type allows the almanac to be programmed thus further simplifying the calculations.
calculations.

Although dedicated mainly towards astro-navigation, these hand-held computers could also be used as straightforward calculators to solve general navigation problems. They can be used for working out ETA's, fuel consumption etc, and they can be a great help in general navigation as well as astro-navigation by handling much of the tedious calculation work. The user has to play an active part in the operation so that a good relationship is built up which gives trust in the results. These hand-held computers are easy to use on a yacht, take up the minimum of space and should find a place in the repertoire of navigation equipment on every yacht, even when more sophisticated equipment is fitted. Because they are self-contained units they can provide a good back-up to the main navigation systems.

A few larger fixed computer units were developed for marine use, but they never really caught on, partly because of their size and cost, and because they offered little more than the hand-held units. At the same time navigation computers began to be incorporated into the electronic position finding system coming on to the market. These computers could perform all the course, position, speed and distance calculations based on waypoints fed into the receiver, but made no attempt to enter the astro-navigation market which was left to the hand-held computer. It is usually possible to link the modern hand-held computer to a small battery-powered printer so that a record of the calculations can be kept for reference.

Tidal Calculations

One area which has been largely ignored by the marine computer market is that of tidal calculations. Many yachtsmen find tides difficult to comprehend and even more difficult to calculate and there would appear to be a requirement for some means of calculating tide heights from the basic time and height information. Such a calculator could not take into account local tidal anomalies which may be one reason for not developing these units.

The logical place for incorporating a tidal calculator is in the echo sounder so that the depth displayed could be related to the chart datum. This would then allow the echo sounder to be integrated with the electronic chart to give a direct comparison between the real and charted depths. With the increased automation of navigation, this comparison could be used as a check and a warning device. Any major difference between the two readings would either indicate that the position finding system or the echo sounder were faulty, or that simply the sea bed had changed considerably. Whichever was the cause, the warning would serve to bring the navigator out of any complacent acceptance of the situation and seek to find a way of checking the position. Checks and warnings of this type will become important with increasing automation in navigation.

One of the main functions of the echo sounder has been a check on progress. By showing the depth it can confirm the position or warn of deteriorating conditions. By adjusting the actual depth to the chart datum the depth reading could have more significance and would fit better into future integrated navigation systems. With the high capacity of modern computers it should be possible to have tide tables, either in a permanent memory or as an accessible disc or cassette memory.

Integrated Electronics

Integrating the individual electronic systems on board a yacht can produce considerable benefits. This is one of the main areas of electronic development and taken to its ultimate, will lead to a single control unit which will incorporate all the individual systems which make up the electronic package. The early stages however of integration usually involve links between two individual units and this is likely to be the initial trend. The basis for the more comprehensive type of integrated system is being laid in some of the integrated sailing efficiency instruments which feed a variety of information into a central computer which in turn displays information derived from the inputs.

The course and speed inputs required for the Transit satnav system are an example of integration, the option being to input this information manually. This same course and speed information can also be obtained from one of the hyperbolic position finding systems and this has led to an interesting form of integration where each navigation receiver upgrades the accuracy of the other by means of a mutually beneficial link.

In a Loran C/satnav combination, the Loran C because of its good repeatable accuracy would provide an accurate course and speed input which would help to upgrade the accuracy of position given by the satnav. This position would then be used as a reference by the Loran C which in turn would help to upgrade the accuracy of the Loran C position. After three or four satellite passes, this interchange of information would lead to a considerably higher accuracy from both receivers, with the Loran C operating in a kind of differential mode based on the satnav reference positions.

This type of position finding integration has been developed by some manufacturers to produce LoranC/satnav and Omega/ satnav combinations. The latter is primarily an ocean navigation system. One type of receiver on the market combines four position finding systems, Loran C, Decca Navigator, Omega and satnav all in one unit, but here the aim is primarily to give worldwide coverage for position finding, with the receiver automatically switching to the best system in relation to the area of navigation. The need for such a piece of equipment emphasises the inadequacies of the existing position finding systems which all have either regional or accuracy limitations. When Navstar GPS becomes available, this one navigation system will eventually take over from all of the existing systems, although we may see a limited use of combined systems which will offer a back-up or a check on the Navstar GPS system.

Improved position accuracy can be one of the benefits of integration. Another can be the automation of functions such as maintaining a desired track. This can be achieved by linking a position finding system with an autopilot with the desired track having been programmed into the position finding system. This type of link can rule out the effects of wind, tide and currents, with the heading of the craft being automatically adjusted to bring it back on to the desired track. This track can be either a great circle or a rhumb line, with the track of the former being automatically programmed.

For sailing yachts, such a system can incorporate a wind reference so that the heading selected takes into account the sailing conditions as well as the desired track.

This type of integration enables the compass to be bypassed to a certain extent. The heading reference is the track which the vessel is to steer and the position finding equipment determines whether the vessel is to the left or right of the track. It will then initiate a small alteration of course to bring the vessel back on track. The sensitivity of the hyperbolic position finding systems in the relative mode enables this to be done with considerable accuracy.

An extension of this integration is to link in a plotter or electronic chart so that the vessel's progress can be seen adn checked on the display. This then gives the navigator most of the information he requires, but the story does not end there. This is where links with the echo sounder and a tidal calculator could be brought in, and with an electronic chart system it could be possible to introduce a form of proximity warning device to indicate a close approach to rocks or shoals. The integration story does not end there and radar is also being brought into the picture.

Integrating Radar

Linking position finding equipment and radar is still in its infancy, but it points the way towards the fully comprehensive integrated navigation systems which will be the inevitable result of current electronic development. One system available uses the radar screen as a form of plotter or electronic chart and the vessel's track can be seen moving across the screen in real time. It is almost as though the navigator has a bird's eye view of his vessel and is looking down on its progress, with the land and other vessels moving past. This type of display contains a great deal of information, but it still requires a considerable amount of interpretation. The basic radar picture has not changed so that navigation marks are not labelled and the radar display of the land may not always conform to the actual land pattern because of shielding. The display still needs to be simplified to make it easier to interpret whilst at the same time more information has to be available to make a comprehensive navigation display.

These requirements have led to the linking of position finding systems, radar and electronic charts into one single unit. With such a wealth of information available an ingenious solution has been used to simplify the display, making it easier to use than a conventional radar display.

Colour is used primarily in the form of an electronic chart of the area showing the coastline and navigation features. This display is shown on a video screen and the radar picture is superimposed on top of the chart display. Where the radar returns from the land and fixed navigation marks coincide with the chart display, the chart display takes precedence. This means that all of the radar returns are suppressed except those from objects which are not shown on the chart ie other vessels and sandbanks or rocks uncovered by the tide. The radar returns which are displayed are shown in a contrasting colour which makes them stand out very clearly making them easy to identify. In harbour use, even ships which are alongside can be clearly identified on the display.

The position input into such a system enables the vessel's track to be seen moving across the display, with automatic adjustment to keep it near the centre. The scale of the chart display can be adjusted manually to suit the conditions and indeed the display can be tailored to meet the specific requirements of the user. Any discrepancy between the chart and the radar due to inaccuracy of the position finding system will soon be apparent to the user by the non-alignment of the chart and radar pictures and can be adjusted manually so that the radar acts as a check on the position finding system.

This type of integrated system probably represents the ultimate in navigation systems for yachts in the foreseeable future. Although primarily a harbour navigation system it can be used for coastal navigation and a suitable range of charts is being developed. It is called Viewnav and has already been developed as a portable unit to be carried on board ships by pilots. This means that the size and power requirements could be matched to those suitable for yacht use. The main application, however, of such equipment is initially seen for ships operating in critical harbour areas. The use of such equipment for yachts may still be a long way off because of cost and complexity. The Viewnav system does give an indication of the direction in which electronic equipment for yachts may be heading.

Comprehensive Integration

The electronics equipment described above represents a fairly complete navigation package but electronics are being used more widely and navigation is only part of the requirement. The integration of electronics is being tackled from a number of different directions and no clear pattern has yet emerged as to which will be the optimum route towards full integration.

For the sailing yacht, the packages of sailing instruments are being linked into central computers to provide a wide range of information. Here the main object is to get the yacht sailing as efficiently as possible. Even where a position finding system is linked in this plays almost a secondary role, with its main function being to provide course and speed made good over the ground. We are, however, seeing the development of these systems to incorporate an autopilot so that the track of the yacht can be planned and the central computer will maintain the yacht on this track as far as practical, using both wind and compass references. Systems are already available which can extend this further by indicating which sails should be set to optimise the performance for the conditions.

One route towards integration for the power yacht, is through engine and fuel monitoring systems. These systems can be used to optimise fuel consumption and progress, and they could be programmed to advise the speed required to arrive at a destination at a set time. Related to a position finding system, the user can be presented with a wide variety of information with which to optimise the performance in relation to requirements.

A computer based unit designed to coordinate a wide range of yacht communications. The same computer can be used for other purposes on board and it enables a businessman to take his work to sea with him.

With both of these systems, which tend to be aimed towards optimising performance, there tends to be a gap between them and the development of pure navigation systems. This is a gap which will close as development progresses. Development work for the ship market is taking place on systems which are all embracing. Instead of being based on individual units linked together the centre of the system is the computer, with raw information from many sources being fed in. The computer software programmes then process this information as required and display it on demand. A single display screen is not likely to be sufficient for all the information required and the trend is towards twin displays, one for navigation and one for performance and monitoring. This is the ideal way but yachts might opt for a single screen with the ability to switch displays.

This type of fully integrated computer-based system moves away from the concept of specialised equipment. Most of the systems of this type being developed are based around standard personal computers which are suitably marinised and equipped with appropriate software programmes. Provided that a suitable high definition display is used, such a computer could be used for the chart display and all the other navigation and monitoring requirements.

Back-up systems

No navigator worth his salt is going to rely entirely on one system. One of the problems with a centralised computer control and monitoring system is that it tends to put all the eggs in one basket. Modern electronics are very reliable but they are not

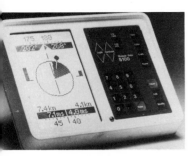

An integrated electronic unit covering most yacht requirements. Different pages of information cover subjects such as position, engine monitoring etc. The one shown covers log, compass and depth with a mixture of analogue and digital displays. Although somewhat confusing at first glance it becomes clearer with use.

infallible. One of the arguments against taking the route towards centralised computers, is that the failure of a small component could lead to a total failure. There is a need to build in redundancy into any system to reduce the effect of any failure. This requires careful planning of any yacht system of integrated electronics.

With a central computer system, one obvious solution is to have two computers, but the demands on space, cost and power supplies probably rule this out. There is therefore some merit in ensuring that the important input information fed into the computer can operate in the 'stand alone' mode. Position finding information for instance, should still be available even if the main computer fails. Although the aspect of convenience may have been lost, there is still information available to allow the yacht to be navigated safely.

With an electronic chart system, the prudent navigator would want to carry paper charts as a back-up, and these would be useful if the position finding system had to be used as a 'stand alone' unit. It could be argued that this need for back-up systems rather defeats the use of fully integrated systems. Certainly many yachtsmen are going to have to consider very carefully just how far they want to go down the route of integration. This route offers convenience and labour saving, but it must be matched by suitable back-up systems or built in redundancy if integrity is to be maintained.

As we move towards fully integrated systems, the manufacturers will ensure the compatibility of the various units and this is one of the attractions of such a system. It is much more difficult to integrate equipment from different manufacturers, although there have been some moves towards fitting compatible outlets to equipment. The National Marine Electronics Association in the USA have been one of the leaders in setting standards for making equipment compatible and because of the absence of any other well defined standards these look set to spread worldwide in due course. These will enable instruments to talk to each other and may enable a suitable half way house of integration to be developed with existing instruments.

With increasing reliance on electronic instrumentation, yachtsmen will have to develop a philosophy towards the use of this equipment. They will have to ensure that back-up systems are available in the event of individual failure and that in the event of an electrical failure, the basic navigation skills have not been discarded. The current intermediate stage in electronic development will force some difficult decisions to be made about how far to rely on electronics and, with increasing integration, just how far one failure will affect the rest of the system.

The precise position information shown on this Loran C receiver may give a misleading impression of its accuracy. This is not a reflection on the receiver but is due to errors in the Loran C system. An indication of the degree of accuracy of navigation displays would be helpful for the navigator.

9 Navigation

Electronics have brought about a considerable change in the techniques of navigation. From having to coax information out of instruments and equipment, the navigator now has the much easier task of simply being presented with information in a usable form which he has to interface with the chart. This has taken many of the tedious steps out of navigation and has made navigation a much more precise art. The navigator, however, still has to have his wits about him because whilst the information may be presented in a very precise way, this may not always be an indication of its accuracy. Indeed one of the disturbing features of modern electronic equipment is that information is presented with little indication of its inherent accuracy. A log may read to 1/10 of a knot, but at best may only be accurate to 1 knot.

The error levels possible with electronic equipment should make the navigator cautious, but equally it is the way in which information is presented that is forcing changes in navigation methods. In the days of compass and watch navigation, the navigator would relate his position to the nearest land because that was what concerned him. Now positions are given in latitude and longitude and navigation is carried out with waypoints. Latitude and longitude positions are used even close to land and this can make quite a change in techniques necessary. The use of bearing and distance to pinpoint a position is disappearing. To many yachtsmen it will seem alien to use latitude and longitude for a position just off a lighthouse, but you have to talk to electronic equipment in a language it will understand.

Position Lines

The basic requirement of all navigation is to know where you are and the position is determined by position lines. Every

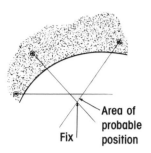

Fix | Area of probable position

Three bearings crossing usually produce a 'cocked hat' which shows the area of probable position. This is only true if the bearings are accurate and reliable.

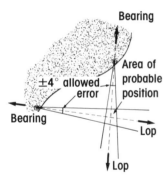

Bearing | ±4° allowed error | Area of probable position | Bearing | Lop | Lop

Where a degree of error can be expected in a bearing, as in a DF bearing then it is better to show the error on the chart so that an area of probable position is determined. This diagram shows the situation with two cross bearings.

electronic instrument will give at least one position line, which is a line somewhere along which the craft lies. The position line does not have to be a straight line, it can be straight, curved, hyperbolic or random. The latter could relate to the information gained from an echo sounder; if it shows 10 fathoms after correction, then the craft is somewhere on the 10-fathom line on the chart.

In itself, this sort of information may not be significant. A position line could be hundreds of miles long, but hopefully you are not that lost. You will have some sort of dead reckoning (DR) position which should narrow the possibilities down a bit. You may have obtained one position line from one piece of equipment and another line can be obtained from another piece, or from a compass bearing.

Things then look brighter, because when two position lines cross you have a position. Its accuracy, however, will depend on the reliability of the two position lines.

A third position line can check the other two, providing they cross reasonably closely in a small 'cocked hat', which is the triangle formed by the three position lines. The size and shape of this triangle will give some idea of the accuracy of the position. The smaller the 'cocked hat' the more accurate the position is likely to be, but this only applies if the position lines cross each other at wide angles; a long narrow triangle should be treated with caution.

Position lines crossing at right angles will be the most accurate because any error in one line will only affect the position by the amount of that error. If the lines cross at a narrow angle then any error will be considerably magnified, and the accuracy of the position obtained will be poor. The diagram will help to make this clearer. One of the reasons why you should have a chart of the position line patterns of Loran C or Decca Navigator is so that you can see the angle at which they cross and so gauge the reliability of the position.

Two other points with position lines. If the line is obtained from a bearing, then it will run from the object taken in the direction found. If the position line is a range or distance, then it will be a circle centred on the object from which the range is taken.

This theory of position lines must be understood if one is going to get the best out of electronic navigation aids. Once grasped it is quite simple and if you can think of the problems in terms of position lines then you are a long way towards using the equipment intelligently. Remember that a craft will be somewhere along a position line and if you have two lines crossing then the craft will be at the intersection.

It is nice to draw a thin line on the chart and say that your craft is somewhere on that line. In reality the line should often be quite broad to allow for the degree of accuracy of the bearing which if taken by RDF, may be only accurate to about four degrees; this puts the craft somewhere in a sector four degrees wide radiating from the radio beacon. Similarly, a vague range will give the position of the craft as somewhere between two concentric circles centred on the bearing object.

Latitude and Longitude

With the latest position finding equipment, the position lines are defined in terms of latitude and longitude. It is a navigator's dream to have positions described in this way where they can be directly plotted on the chart. Such positions have all the attributes of a good fix. The position lines cross at right angles. In reality, however, the position has been translated into latitude and longitude from position lines which may be hyperbolic in the case of Loran C, Decca Navigator or Omega, or ranges and bearings in the case of satnav. One of the problems with this translation is that it gives no indication of the angle in which the original position lines cross and so the sensitivity of the fix to errors cannot be easily judged.

With the hyperbolic systems, the lines of position can be obtained on special overprinted charts and if you want a higher degree of accuracy and a better appreciation of the quality of the fix then these charts should be used. Most yachtsmen, however, are likely to use the standard chart and the latitude/longitude positions. This ties in well with waypoint navigation which we shall deal with later and latitude and longitude is becoming the standard format for position reference for yacht navigation. This represents a change from the time-honoured range and bearing method and could well lead to changes in chart design to facilitate plotting procedures.

One of the advantages of the hyperbolic systems using the overprinted charts was that positions could be plotted on charts by simple interpolation between the printed lines. Chart publishers are now considering printing a much denser latitude and longitude grid on their charts so that plotting can be done by hand without the need for instruments. This will be a great boon for yachtsmen where space is often very limited for plotting and conditions are rarely easy. Of course the electronic chart overcomes this problem by plotting automatically.

Latitude and longitude is one of the very few fully international position grids so it is logical to use it as a position reference for navigation. Position finding instruments are programmed to calculate courses and distances between specified points and the use of latitude and longitude gives positions to these instruments

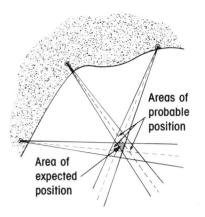

With three cross bearings one is presented with an area of probable position and an area of expected position. With DF bearings, the possible error could be as much as 10 degrees which can give a large area of expected position.

in a language which they can readily understand. Certainly, sooner or later yachtsmen will have to switch to this position reference and the switch will be hastened when the Navstar GPS system comes into widespread use.

Waypoint Navigation

With a position finding system producing positions in latitude and longitude the logical step to take full advantage of this is to switch the navigation system on board to waypoint navigation. To a certain extent, this form of navigation is very similar to that previously carried with the main change being to define positions or waypoints on the course in terms of latitude and longitude.

Almost without exception all the position finding receivers have a facility to operate waypoint navigation. The course you wish to follow is defined in terms of the waypoints where the course is altered. Each of these waypoints is fed into the receiver which then takes over, giving all the information required to navigate the yacht manually or through the autopilot. The receiver can be called on to display the course and distance to the next waypoint so that the navigator is continually aware of any divergence from the set course. This divergence may also be displayed as a distance off-course to right or left. In addition the speed and course made good over the ground can be obtained and from this it is easy for the computer to give an ETA at the current speed.

All this is made easy by waypoint navigation. In addition to the waypoints which have been fed in as points on the course, the computer takes the present position of the yacht as another waypoint. Courses and distances between any two waypoints can be called up so the only information which has to be transferred from the chart is the latitude and longitude of the waypoints.

This can be a tedious task and can be made much easier with an electronic chart system fitted with a cursor. If the positions have to be taken from the paper chart, then over a season of sailing a large store of waypoints will have been gathered and where the receiver has a large waypoint capacity, these can all be numbered and stored for future use. If this system is adopted it is sensible to check the planned courses on the paper chart to make sure that they do not pass over or close to any dangers.

Apart from its ease of use, waypoint navigation has the advantage that all of the planning and most of the work can be done in the comfort of harbour or with portable receivers at home. There is less chance of making mistakes under these conditions and with the receiver fully programmed you will be well prepared for navigation if overtaken by bad weather. Having the courses and waypoints marked on the chart provides a useful reference and check and it is wise not to place too much trust in the position finding receiver and always to check the position by visual observations, soundings or back-up electronic systems such as RDF or radar.

Making a Landfall

Making a landfall is always one of the critical parts of navigation. It is the time when the navigator is put to the test, and the success or otherwise of his navigation is there for all to see. A landfall can be made in a number of ways; at the side of a headland after crossing a bay, at a port entrance after an open sea crossing, at a fairway buoy or at a lighthouse or lightvessel. When using waypoint navigation each waypoint is likely to involve a landfall of one type or another.

The techniques for making a landfall will vary with the equipment available and the visibility. The geography of the landfall will also have a bearing on the approach and the type of landfall will have to be taken into consideration. The distance covered since the last visual fix must be considered because this will determine the degree of error which might be expected in the DR position.

To the navigator of a yacht equipped with radar and an electronic position finding system this may seem an excessively cautious approach to making a landfall. The position finding system should get the yacht close enough in safety and the radar provides a good back-up even if the visibility deteriorates. However the cautious navigator always has something up his sleeve and if the landfall is chosen carefully, it can still be made in safety in poor visibility even if there is an electrical or electronic failure.

Approaching a headland from across a bay, the course should be set inside the headland. There will then be little danger of passing outside and missing it altogether in poor visibility. Try and choose a stretch of the coastline to make the landfall on where there are no off-lying dangers so that it can be approached with the echo sounder running and there will be ample warning as the coast is closed. Here it is sensible to approach the coast at an angle so that if something unexpected looms out of the fog, then there is only one logical way to alter course. Approaching at right angles to the coastline doubles the choice and at the same time makes a sharper turn necessary to get out of danger.

With a position finding system or radar, the approach need not be so cautious, but the check with the echo sounder should be a fundamental part of the navigation technique. The same sort of approach should be made when attempting a landfall at a buoy, lighthouse or lightvessel or when making a harbour entrance. Study the chart of the area very carefully to find an area which will give a check on your approach so that you don't rely entirely on an electronic position finding system. This check could be a section of clear coastline, a deep water channel or even a shoal with adequate water over it. If you angle your approach so that you can use the echo sounder as a check in this way, you can narrow the element of risk and have a second stage to your navigation system so that if the primary system lets you down you are not totally lost. In fine weather, this second stage navigation is easily provided by visual checks, but navigation in poor visibility becomes much more critical and you should use every clue available rather than rely blindly on the output from the electronic instruments.

Radar for Navigation

There are two main requirements in navigation: to know where you are and to know where you are going. Radar can provide both of these requirements, provided that there are identifiable targets on the display. Position finding can be by two methods, ranges or bearings, or by a combination of both. Ranges should be used in preference to bearings because of their greater accuracy, and every navigator using radar should equip himself with a pair of compasses so that ranges can be quickly and easily plotted on the chart.

The movement of a small craft in a seaway not only reduced the accuracy of the bearings obtained by radar, but it also makes it more difficult to plot them. Parallel rules require two hands adn a large flat surface; requirements which are often hard to find on a yacht. The compasses which are required for plotting ranges can be manipulated with one hand, and at a pinch these could be plotted with the chart folded on your knees.

A position can be obtained with only two ranges but such a fix must always be suspect, because an error in either of the ranges used or any error in plotting them will affect the position and there is no check on the accuracy. Using three ranges gives a much better indication of the accuracy of the fix. If all three ranges intersect or nearly intersect at one point then the position can be used reliably, provided, and this is a very important proviso, that the ranges are all from positively identified targets.

To obtain good fixes using radar ranges, it is important to make a direct comparison between the chart and the radar display. This will enable features on the radar display to be identified readily but be careful about making hasty assumptions. It is all too easy to make the radar display fit what you expect to see and when making a landfall, the first targets to show up may be high land behind the coastline which can give a distorted view.

If a good fix is obtained by means of three ranges this gives the navigator the chance to make a position identification of other targets because he can measure the range from a known position. In practice a fix is obtained using three known ranges and at the same time a couple of ranges are taken of other points on the display which are thought to be identifiable features. After the three positive ranges are plotted, the others are plotted and if they pass through the position this gives reasonable proof of identification. The prudent navigator will check two or three times before he relies on them. By using this method when coasting, the navigator is obtaining a fix and at the same time identifying new targets which can be brought into use for position finding as the vessel moves along the coast. On a coastline which has many headlands this method of frequent position finding enables the navigator to keep a check on the headlands as they pass and avoid confusing one with another, an all too easy mistake to make on some coastlines. A further check can be made on the positions obtained by relating them to the speed of the boat after making due allowance for tides.

Ranges are normally taken from headlands because these are usually clearly defined and easy to identify. Not all coastlines, however, are so conveniently arranged and other targets have to be used. A straight stretch of coastline can provide a distance-off which it may be possible to combine with the range of an identified target, but such a position should be treated with a bit more caution. Just the distance-off can give a useful guide because this is usually the critical measurement when coasting. Confirmation of the distance-off can often be had from the echo sounder, but a lot depends on sea bed features and the steepness of the bottom slope from the shore.

Ranges from buoys and lightvessels can be used for position fixing, but should be used with caution for two reasons. Firstly, it is not so easy to get positive identification from these targets, as they look the same as other vessels on the display. Secondly, their position is only approximate as they are moored by a single chain and they are liable to drag. Beacons and isolated lighthouses are excellent for position fixing provided that they can be identified clearly, but they are not particularly good radar targets.

Sandbanks will show up on the radar display at close ranges. It is usually the broken water around the edge which returns the strongest echo, and this could be used for fixing. But remember that the position of the edge of the bank will vary with the height of the tide and with the sea state. Rough seas will make the waves break further out. The same applies to gently shelving beaches where there can be a distance of several cables between the high and low water marks. Such beaches are often stabilised with groynes which are marked on the chart and usually show quite clearly on the display.

Whilst fixing gives the navigator his present position and enables him to determine what progress his vessel has made, he also wants to know what is going to happen in the future, ie where his vessel is going to go. Course and speed will give him this information to a certain extent, but there are many occasions, particularly when coasting, when he wants to know where he is going in relation to a fixed object. This is the case when rounding a headland with off-lying dangers or when passing a shoal. The same applies when navigating in a buoyed channel. When conditions allow, the navigator can often assess where he is going in relation to a fixed object by visual observation, but this involves a certain amount of estimation of distances and there is always an element of doubt.

Radar is the only navigation aid which can show the effect of a proposed course in relation to a fixed object. When approaching a headland with off-lying dangers a course may be required which keeps the craft one mile off. This could be achieved by continuous position fixing and adjusting of the course, but it can also be done by measuring the distance between the heading market and the headland in question, and setting this to one mile by varying the course. This will not take into account any set of the tide, but it is a simple matter to check for this as progress is made along the course. If the distance between the heading marker and the headland reduces then the craft is being set in and an alteration of course to seaward would be appropriate.

This simple method of navigation is equally effective in buoyed channels where the heading marker can be lined up directly on the next buoy in the channel, or to keep that buoy a certain distance off as appropriate. This is conditional on the fact that the buoy can be clearly identified, and this reinforces the point that this system should be backed up by alternative position fixing wherever possible.

Another case where it can be used with good effect is when entering harbour, particularly one you are not familiar with. It is often difficult to identify a harbour entrance from seaward, particularly at night when the many shore lights can make it difficult to identify the navigation lights. By presenting a plan view, radar can make it easy to pick out piers and entrances and by lining up the heading marker in relation to these it is possible to make a confident approach.

This system of navigation requires no chartwork except for identifying features and for measuring the required distances off. It can be done simply by study of the display and this makes it particularly suited for use in adverse weather when the motion of the craft can make navigation difficult.

The radar can be very useful when coming into an anchorage, particularly when two VRMs are available. The position of the desired anchorage from two radar identifiable objects on shore can be measured from the chart, and the distance off from these targets measured on the radar will give a clear indication of the approach to the anchorage.

Navigating successfully with radar required considerable practice in order to build up confidence. Practice in fine weather will give the confidence to use the equipment reliably in poor visibility and this practice is even more important when it comes to collision avoidance.

Radar for Collision Avoidance

The way radar is used in poor visibility will depend a great deal on just what the visibility is like, on the sea conditions and on the manoeuvrability of the craft to which it is fitted. The first and last factors have much in common because if an approaching vessel can be sighted in good time to take avoiding action, then the job of the radar operator is made much easier. All he has to do is give notice of approaching vessels so that a visual sighting can be made at the earliest possible moment. It sounds easy but in fact there are many snags which can lead to danger.

The first is that the range of visibility may fluctuate. You may be able to see for a half mile which should give you ample time to get out of the way when you sight the other vessel. What happens though, if the visibility suddenly closed in just when you expect to sight the approaching craft? There is no time to take alternative action and you will probably make a panic manoeuvre, a thing to be avoided in fog. Very rarely is the visibility in fog constant and you must always be prepared for variations.

Another snag is that there may possibly be two or more vessels approaching from different directions and your manoeuvre to avoid one may take you into the path of another. You must remember also that you are a small craft and therefore a poor echo on the other vessel's radar if he has one. He will not thank you if you suddenly appear on his screen a short distance ahead. Remember he does not know what your intentions are and whether you have radar. In bad weather, the return from your vessel could easily be lost in the sea clutter after he has initially detected you. The same applies to your radar. There is no guarantee that it will detect all the vessels in your vicinity, so you must proceed with a degree of caution and be prepared for the unexpected. The law requires that you keep a good look-out in fog, and heaven help the person who does not.

Most yachts will be using a relative motion radar. With this type, your vessel remains at the centre of the display and other targets move past. Now, because you are moving as well, but apparently stationary on the screen, other vessels will seem to move on the display with a combination of your course and speed and theirs. All the movement is transferred to the target leaving you stationary in the centre. This means that there is no quick means of measuring the course and speed of the other vessel and plotting is the recommended solution. Plotting means taking the range and bearing of other targets at frequent intervals and plotting them out on special plotting sheets. The course and speed of your vessel are then applied to find out what the other vessel is doing.

This is certainly not a task to carry out on board a yacht tossing around at sea, so what can be done in terms of collision avoidance for yachts?

Anything you can do to reduce the number of vessels you have to contend with will help the situation, and this applies particularly to ships which because of their size and poor manoeuvrability are not things with which you want to tangle in fog. You cannot actually get rid of the ships — they have as much right to be there as you have — but you can keep away from them. Ships tend to follow set courses between harbours and ports and, while in the open sea their movement appears to be a bit more random, it is possible to set your course to avoid the obvious shipping lanes. If you have to cross the main shipping routes in the open sea then try to do so at right angles to the route. By this means you will get across in the shortest possible time and if necessary you can wait for a gap in the shipping before crossing. With shipping approaching on your beam it is much easier to identify its behaviour.

When you are coasting there is likely to be shipping doing the same thing, but in general ships keep at least two miles off headlands. In a small craft you are quite safe to pass the headland a lot closer provided of course there are no off-lying dangers or tide races. Even then ships usually allow a generous safety margin around headlands leaving you clear room to make an inside passage.

Once round the headland ships will set a straight course for the next headland. This is the shortest distance, and time is money to them. If you set your course slightly into the bay then you should keep clear of all the shipping. Another point to remember is that commercial ships generally have a fairly deep draught, certainly in comparison with the average small craft and there are many areas of shallow water which are quite safe for small craft, but which the ships will give a wide berth. You may have to go out of your way a little to make use of some of these, but the increased peace of mind makes it worthwhile, and you may be able to make better speed.

The same applies when you are entering harbour or using buoyed channels. The buoys are laid to mark the deep water channel which is for the use of shipping. Almost invariably there is an area of shallower water outside the main channel, and this is perfectly suitable for small craft. If you want to hop from buoy to buoy in the channel to keep a check on your position by visual observation, then you can do this on the side away from the deep water.

When entering harbour there will come a time when you will probably have to mix with the big ships, but fog usually restricts the movements of these vessels in harbour much more than it does small craft and there should not be any difficulty. You can be sure that any shipping will be moving very slowly in enclosed waters, the only exception being ferry boats which have a habit of ploughing along at full speed irrespective of visibility. The only consolation to take is that these craft follow regular tracks which can often be gleaned from the charts, and that they know the waters so well that they will be aware of your presence.

One point to remember when entering harbour is that you may need time to stop and sort things out. If there are several echoes ahead of which you are not sure, then stop and work things out rather than plough on and hope they will become clear. If there are tides then the tidal streams will still be affecting you and for this reason, when the visibility is poor, it is much better to enter harbour on the ebb tide and leave on the flood. This enables you to stop and sort things out by stemming the tide. In this way you can keep control of your craft and there is no risk of you being swept into dangers ahead.

Stemming the tide also enables you to stop in relation to the ground whilst still maintaining your craft on her heading. This keeps a better radar picture because when your craft starts to swing, as she will do once you stop altogether, all the echoes on the display will swing round and create a very confused picture for a while, just when you want it clear to sort things out.

What you need to know from the information shown on the display is which of the approaching echoes you can safely ignore and which you will have to try to get more information about. Any echoes which are moving away from the centre of the screen will be moving away from you. The ones you need to worry about are those which are moving towards the centre or some point near the centre.

The classic way of doing this is to take a bearing of the approaching echo. If the bearing does not appreciably change then there is a risk of collision if you both maintain your courses and speeds. It is a simple matter with radar to set the bearing cursor onto the approaching echo and any change in the bearing will soon become apparent. If the bearing opens up on the bow, then the other vessel will pass to the side of you but if it closes towards the ahead position then it will pass ahead of you.

You may well think that this will be all the information required to find out what the other vessel is doing, but there are several points to remember. Bearings can often be unreliable on a small craft. If it is swinging about then it may be difficult to get a good assessment of any change of bearing. Another point to consider is how much of a change of bearing is required before it can be considered safe. A vessel approaching on a reciprocal course will only change its bearing very slowly at first, yet it may still pass a mile away when it is abeam.

In the last case, the bearing will only start to alter appreciably once the range has been closed considerably and this emphasises the need to watch the bearing all the time, because up till now we have been assuming that the approaching vessel has been maintaining a steady course and speed. Any change in either of these will affect the bearing. Try to put yourself in the position of the person in charge of the other vessel. He may have picked up the echo of your craft on his radar and decided that the two vessels are on a collision course. This may have prompted him to alter course to avoid such a situation. Only constant watching of the bearing will determine this, and then only some time after the alteration has been made.

Making an alteration of course or speed to avoid a collision can only be done with any degree of safety by carrying out plotting procedures and, as we have seen, this is not really feasible in small craft. Unless you have a very good reason you are better to maintain your course and speed to avoid confusing other people. One of the problems with the many small boats now being fitted with radar is that there will be a lot of undisciplined manoeuvring of these craft in poor visibility, resulting in confusion.

Maintaining your course and speed also helps you to maintain control of the situation. Any alteration in your course of speed will be reflecting in the behaviour of the echoes on your display and the steadier you can keep the situation the more fully you will be in control of it.

One of the prime objectives of plotting is to determine the point of nearest approach of the other vessel. If two positions of the echo from the vessel are plotted, the extended line joining them will show how closely the two vessels will pass, provided both maintain their course and speed. A simple estimation of this can be made on the radar screen if an initial position is marked by the intersection of the bearing cursor and the variable range marker. After a suitable time interval it is then possible to join this point to the new position of the echo by an imaginary line and get some idea of the point of nearest approach. If no variable range marker is fitted then you can wait until the echo crosses a range ring. This type of mental plotting is a valuable method of assessing approaching echoes particularly when vessels are crossing.

When vessels are approaching from ahead or nearly ahead, the change of bearing is unlikely to give a clear indication of the other vessel's movements. This is one of the commonest types of encounter as most vessels tend to follow set routes along coasts or channels. Because the vessels are closing each other the time for action will be limited and a rapid assessment of the situation is needed. By lining up the cursor with the heading line it is possible to determine whether the approaching echo is closing towards your course or passing on a reciprocal course.

By keeping out of the shipping lanes you can hopefully reduce the number of echoes on the screen which concern you. By using one of the above methods you can eliminate some of the others, except that they must still be watched closely in case they start doing strange things. By this system you can simplify your work and concentrate on those approaching echoes which refuse to keep clear. Hopefully, this will only be one at a time.

At what range you start showing real concern for an approaching vessel depends on many factors. The range of visibility is one, but do not depend on this remaining constant. The speed and manoeuvrability of your own craft is another. The type of approaching vessel is a third, and this can often be determined from the appearance of the echo particularly at the short ranges. A ship will show as a much larger echo at close quarters than small boats and, generally speaking, the manoeuvrability of a vessel decreases as its size increases. Remember also that ships generally take action in fog by altering course rather than speed, because course alterations are quicker and thus more effective. Small craft respond more readily to their throttles and this can be made use of.

Any vessel coming to within one mile should give cause for concern and you should consider taking action. The logical course is to stop the engines, which serves the dual purpose of buying time and giving quiet so that you can listen for the fog signal of the approaching vessel. Rather than take the way off the vessel completely it is better to keep the picture stabilised. A close-quarters situation is not one where you want the picture going round in circles. A very close watch should be kept on the display and the bearing of the approaching vessel checked continually. In many circumstances, the change in speed will be sufficient to enable two craft, which were previously on collision courses, to pass clear.

At this stage it is a good idea to call out the range of the approaching vessel. The look-out will know what the visibility is like and he will be able to give warning if it starts to close in as the other vessel approaches. The other vessel should be navigating with equal caution so that when a sighting is finally made, there will be ample time to take any necessary avoiding action.

Visibility at sea rarely gets less than the stopping distance of most small craft, particularly when they are alert and ready to take action. The situation is different with large ships where visibility of 400 yards might mean that the navigator cannot see his own bow let alone stop and manoeuvre. For a small craft this distance would give space to do a complete turn or come to a halt even without warning.

It is always difficult to anticipate the actions of other vessels which are approaching in fog. Their actions cannot be determined from the radar for some while after they have been taken and if you are altering course or speed at the same time, then it is even more difficult. There is always the possibility of you both altering course together, possibly worsening the situation. This is why it is always better to slacken speed which hopefully serves the double purpose of removing the collision menace and of buying time to sort things out.

If the visibility is really poor you must feel your way past the other vessel at very slow speed relying on both the radar information and the other vessel's fog signal to locate him. With radar there is more incentive to do this than in pre-radar days when the only means of navigation in fog was a timed run and any slowing down would throw your DR calculations out. Now the position can be quickly re-established once the danger of collision is past. There is always the worry that an approaching vessel seen on the display, particularly if it has the appearance of a ship, has not detected your echo on his radar and is ploughing on regardless, thinking that he has a clear sea in front of him. I know it shouldn't happen but that is no consolation to you when you are in the water with a smashed-up boat around you. Any echo which is closing more rapidly than the visibility seems to dictate should be viewed with caution. If you are going to alter course do so boldly and early, but if you take the course suggested above of slowing right down or stopping, you will have a better idea of his speed of approach. One way out of the dilemma is to turn so that the echo of the approaching ship is right astern, and then increase speed. This will increase the time available before collision becomes imminent, and give you time to establish his course and speed so that you can take avoiding action.

Such a manoeuvre will waste some of your time, but you must expect this in poor visibility. What you lack in the capability of your radar set and facilities you must make up with the good manoeuvrability and control at your disposal. Most of the problems concerning collision avoidance in fog will stem from encounters between small craft and ships because of their differing capabilities and lack of understanding. Encounters between two small craft should not pose too much difficulty, but you should never assume that the other craft has radar. If he has not then he will probably be navigating with a great deal more caution than you are, and if it gets really thick he will probably anchor.

With small craft encounters you must be on your guard against small craft echoes being lost in the sea clutter. An echo of a small craft is sometimes picked up beyond the sea clutter only to be lost within the clutter. Careful adjustment of the set may reveal it again, but if not then you must navigate with great caution and adjust your speed accordingly. This applies at all times. Having radar on board does not give you the right to charge along at high speed.

So far we have considered the problem of collision avoidance when the other vessels which are causing you concern come along conveniently one at a time. If you keep out of the shipping lanes as suggested earlier, you could find this to be the case, but sooner or later you are going to find two or more vessels, which are going to pass close, coming along at the same time. Here you have to be extra careful because in trying to avoid one you may run slap into the other one. You must also consider the possibility of the other two vessels altering course or speed to avoid each other.

This is where early assessment can be vital. If this situation occurs when crossing a shipping lane, then wait and let the other two sort themselves out. In this way the three vessel situation becomes a two vessel situation and is much easier to resolve. If one vessel is ahead and the other is crossing then it will usually be much easier to predict the movement of the vessel coming from ahead. Again stopping to let the other two sort themselves out can simplify the situation to your advantage. You could make a bold alteration of course and if you made this towards the crossing vessel so as to pass astern, it could provide a solution but remember he might have the same idea and alter to pass astern of you. This could leave you with a rapidly deteriorating situation.

Stopping a small craft is a simple, safe expedient either to solve or at least give more time to solve the movements of approaching ships. Remember that once you are stopped, the movements of the other echoes will reflect their true courses and speeds making it much easier to predict their intentions. In the sort of close-quarters work which has to be used when making approaches to harbours or other congested waters, you must expect to have to stop or slow down every now and then, to give a chance to assess the situation.

Judging what is a safe speed in fog will depend on many circumstances. You should be able to stop within less than half the range of visibility. Certainly anything over 10 knots is not recommended where the visibility is less than ¼ mile. Proceeding under sail in fog is not recommended. Even if you have sufficient wind you will lack the necessary control to manoeuvre effectively and the sails will block a clear view ahead. Even with radar in use you should continue to sound your fog signal.

Using a radar range of 2-3 miles will probably be best in fog. This enables you to concentrate on the nearby vessels without worrying about those further away. Try to avoid switching ranges, although you may need a longer range occasionally for navigation purposes.

Collision avoidance in fog presents probably the greatest challenge to the yachtsman. Current small boat radars rarely provide sufficient information to proceed with confidence although some yacht radar manufacturers are now addressing this problem. This could be one of the main areas of development in future yacht radar and the use of software controlled radard will make these developments easier. There will, however, be no easy solution and caution should be the watchword in fog.

Accuracy

With position finding systems prescribing their levels of accuracy, the temptation is for the yacht navigator to work closely to these limits. If you are navigating in clear weather where a visual check can back up the electronic information then no problems arise, but perhaps you want to pass close to a sandbank or submerged rock which cannot be seen. Here natural caution should prevail and you should allow yourself adequate margins.

Even though modern electronic systems are very reliable even when operating under the difficult conditions found on board some yachts you must be prepared for failures. A temporary interruption of power on board may lead to a loss of position information from which it may take the receiver some time to recover. Signals from the shore can also be interrupted so the general rule should be never to get yourself into a position with electronic navigation which you cannot get out of by using traditional methods. Try not to use the advertised accuracy levels to the ultimate and always keep a margin in hand to cater for the unexpected.

During racing it may be
necessary to read
electronic displays from
some distance away and
this large clear format
display is designed for
this role.

10 Racing

The navigation techniques used for yacht racing using electronic equipment are similar in many respects to those used for general navigation, with one big difference. In yacht racing you seek to gain maximum advantage, to cut corners, and this means stretching the capabilities of electronics to the limit. Here you can accept the risk of reduced margins, but by the same token, you will not win a race by going aground, so the navigator has to understand the limitations of his equipment very well.

Navigation is just one facet of the way in which electronics can help. Sailing efficiency can be improved considerably with electronic sensing and computing and this has been taken to extremes in the sophisticated computer systems used on board the 12 metre yachts. Electronics can also play their part in weather forecasting and route planning. The role of electronics in racing is developing rapidly to the point where it is being used to replace traditional skills. Used intelligently, electronics can be a great help in racing. Whether they are allowed to take over almost completely depends on the individual skipper, but there should be a middle road where the electronics and the crew work in harmony to keep the yacht sailing at its optimum for the conditions and the course.

Course Planning

Electronic position finding systems are now used extensively on racing yachts, even for round-the-buoys racing. Loran C and Decca Navigator, with their continuously updated positions, are better for this purpose where good coverage exists, but satnav can also be useful as it reduces the time during which the yacht is sailing on DR. Loran C and Decca Navigator can be used for round-the-buoys racing and the accuracy can be upgraded by checking the errors against a known position before the race starts. Provided the race is only in a local area and does not extend into the night, these errors will remain reasonably consistent and can be applied throughout the race to optimise the courses steered.

One of the advantages of using these position finding systems is that waypoint navigation can be used. The marks of the course will be the main waypoints to be programmed into the receiver, and it may be necessary to add in extra waypoints if the course takes in narrow channels or other areas where navigation is restricted by shoals or coastline. Much of this planning work can be done before the race starts although there may be hectic moments if there are last minute course changes. Once programmed the receiver will give the optimum courses and distances between the waypoint which can help to save time in changing situations.

From this basis, the actual position of the yacht during the race will provide an additional waypoint for calculation during the race. From this waypoint and the next programmed one, the receiver will be able to give a continuous readout of the course required to be made good to the next mark of the course, and the distance to go — information of great value to the navigator in planning his tactics. Used in conjunction with the sailing efficiency instruments, this information can determine the optimum point at which to tack to lay a mark. This distance either side of the rhumb line course between two waypoints will also be displayed by the position finding receiver and this can be a useful guide when tacking although some receivers will only show the distance off the rhumb line to a limited amount.

Because the position finding system is displaying actual positions, it is possible to determine the effects of leeway and tides or currents. Rather than estimate these factors, a much more precise measurement can be made of set and drift, and this in turn can be very sueful for the planning of tactics. It must be remembered that these parameters as displayed are based on historical information and account must be made of anticipated changes in tidal and wind conditions.

If satnav is the only electronic position finding system available, then care will be needed when using it during racing. The 1½-2 hours between fixes will mean that the position is only updated at these intervals and the displayed position will be based on DR in between. Some receivers can correct the DR position with set and drift factors derived from earlier fixes, but care is necessary to identify the different positions displayed and to use them accordingly. Mistakes can also be made between true and magnetic courses and this applies to all receivers. If possible it is best to work all courses in either true or magnetic to avoid confusion. Some receivers allow the magnetic variation to be applied automatically so that all courses displayed are magnetic. This saves one step in the calculations and reduces the chance of mistakes when working under pressure.

Sailing Efficiency and Computers

Probably the biggest application of sailing efficiency instruments is on racing yachts. In particular the trim speed variation is used to ensure that the yacht is sailing at its maximum speed for the prevailing conditions and the effects of any change can be quickly recognised. The VMG is the other important instrument and this optimises the performance in relation to the desired track to windward. Used in conjunction with the course to the next waypoint obtained from the position finding system, the point at which to alter course to lay the next mark can be clearly determined.

Whilst the sailing efficiency instruments show the yacht sailing at its maximum during the race, the information they give out is only going to be of real value if a great deal of testing and tuning has been done before the yacht starts racing. These same sailing efficiency instruments can be used to develop polar diagrams to show the performance of the yacht on different headings with different wind strength, and with different sail combinations. Also coming into this equation is the set of the mast and rigging and the trim and angle of heel of the yacht. The number of variables and the possible combinations are almost infinite but this is just the sort of information a computer can handle.

A suitable computer programme could assess all of these variables and come up with the optimum setting of the variable parameters to suit the particular conditions and course. Such a programme would rely heavily on input from a long series of trials and would only be as reliable as this basic information. A considerable amount of raw data would have to be obtained as the data base. From this the computer could interpolate to show the optimum combination of variable factors for the conditions. A spreadsheet capability could also be included which would show the effect of altering one of the variable factors on the others.

This is the type of computer programme which is being used on the 12 metres and is finding its way into other top racing boats. Taken to its ultimate such a system, when linked to a position finding system, would dictate which sails were appropriate to the conditions and which was the optimum course to steer for the next mark. It would also be possible to assess the sail and course requirements to the following mark before rounding the one ahead, allowing the necessary preparations to be made.

With such a computer system, the speed trim and the VMG meters still have value for the necessary fine tuning which is carried out all the time. The set of the sheets and the mast and rigging adjustment can be continuously fine tuned. The computer itself is linked directly to the sailing efficiency instruments so that it can monitor the performance and improve the data base all the time.

Back-up Systems

The importance of position finding equipment in racing is easy to appreciate. It has made the navigator's job much easier in many respects and it takes much of the worry out of the job. But with so much information available, he can have a full time job taking advantage of the information. The possibility of failure of this equipment at a critical time during the race must be entertained and some form of back-up is essential.

The easy solution would be to return to the use of the RDF receiver and intensive DR calculations. Certainly there is a good case for keeping a DR plot going all the time as a back-up to the main system and the RDF can sit in the corner to be dusted off as a checking system. The comparative low cost, however, of electronic navigation receivers makes it worth considering the installation of a secondary system. If a Loran C or Decca Navigator is the primary system then a satnav could provide the secondary system. This could be operating and programmed ready to go for the particular course. The opportunity of interfacing the two receivers, as described in earlier chapters, is worth considering for the upgrading of the possible position accuracy.

When Navstar GPS comes into operation and low cost yacht receivers become available this will almost certainly take over as the primary navigation system for racing yachts. It offers a much more consistent level of accuracy than current systems and, with worldwide coverage, it will be particularly useful for yachts participating in international events. Loran C or Decca Navigator will make a good back-up system for Navstar GPS but with any back-up system you must be prepared to face the dilemma of which one to trust if they display a marked difference in their readouts. The echo sounder has an important role to play in racing yachts mainly as a check on the position finding system. It can be particularly valuable when trying to cut corners in shallow water but remember that it only shows the depth immediately under the yacht with no warning of what lies ahead so an echo sounder showing the trend can be a valuable tool. At the high angles of heel and speeds or racing yachts, transducer installation will have to be thought out very carefully to maintain consistent readings.

IOR ratings and Allowances

With IOR racing, the handicaps have a considerable influence on the result. Whilst it is possible to know the IOR rating of an opposing yacht and hence its rating in relation to your own yacht, it can be important to know what it means in terms of rating allowance if the other yacht is one mile ahead. Under the different systems that operate under the IOR system (some working on a time/time basis) it is not always easy to compare the performance of your own yacht with other yachts sighted. If as you should be, you are sailing flat out, there is probably not much you can do about catching up anyway but it can be a boost for crew morale to know if you are ahead on handicap.

Calculators with special programmes based on IOR ratings are now available just for this purpose. Once they have been given the ratings of other yachts and that of your own, they can produce a predicted performance comparison at any stage of a race. In addition to morale boosting this information can be useful to decide the level of risk you are prepared to take. If you hear that the first boat has crossed the line and you can work out your time allowance, it will help to decide what risks are justified in trying to get to the finish. These programmes can also be useful when tuning up against another yacht.

Wind and Weather Planning

Electronics can be a great help in getting your yacht around a course by optimising the navigation and the sailing performance of the yacht, but there is still the question of the wind and weather to consider. You want to know whether the wind is going to back or veer or whether it is going to get stronger or weaker. This information can help you plan your sailing strategy on a long or short race. You will not be able to control the wind, but knowing what it is going to do helps you anticipate the situation.

Electronics can help with weather forecasts both over the radio and through weather fax equipment. The prevailing wind and weather can be assessed through the appropriate measuring

An HF radio which can give worldwide communications. The three component package gives installation flexibility with operator access only required to the compact control panel in the foreground.

instruments and converted to true wind speed and directions. Relating these two factors can lead to a considerable upgrading of your picture of the weather, although it will need some experience of weather to do this. This latter factor is one area where the computer cannot help you very much.

The weather forecasts tend to give a fairly accurate picture of the weather pattern, but they are often inaccurate as regards time. There may be a front moving across the course of the race, heralding a change in the wind direction. It can be critical to your race strategy to know when this change is going to occur and the best indication is the prevailing weather and the way it is changing. The radio and instruments can help here, but it is only the personal observation and personal assessment which can complete the picture. It is possible for satellite weather pictures to be transmitted directly to ships, but the on-board equipment is large and complex. We may see more compact units as development proceeds and such real time information about weather patterns would be invaluable to yacht racing, but this must be several years away yet.

A fully fledged satcom terminal giving both telex and telephone communications world-wide. Whilst the antenna requirements for this communications systems only make it suitable for large yachts at present future size reductions will widen the application.

11 Hear and speak

The ability to talk via radio with people on shore and in other vessels at sea has been one of the major benefits from the development of marine electronics. Radio has also made a tremendous contribution to safety. Some yachtsmen go to sea simply to escape the convenience of modern communications and to obtain peace and quiet, but even these yachtsmen cannot deny this safety aspect of reliable communications.

Radio communication not only allows you to indicate that you have a problem, but also state what the problem is and discuss a solution. Without radio you have to resort to flares or other distress signals to draw attention to your predicament, thus bringing the full force of the rescue services to your aid when all you may need is some more fuel. Radio can provide the link which allows just the right degree of help to be provided.

Radio can do much more. You can find out if a berth is available in a marina before entering. You can obtain weather forecasts, be made aware of navigation problems; in fact it can provide many of the services which we now take for granted on land, and expect when we go to sea. The ability to make direct and reliable telephone and telex calls from a yacht means that a businessman can work from his yacht, not be forced to remain at his office desk. The variety and complexity of yacht radios available today means that equipment is available for every requirement. The main problem is selecting the right equipment for the job.

VHF Radio

It was the advent of low cost VHF radios which really started the radio revolution on yachts. The yachtsmen now has an easy-to-use cheap means of communication. VHF radio can operate anywhere between 30 and 300MHz but certain areas of this wide frequency band are reserved for selected users. The standard marine VHF frequencies are between 156 and 163MHz with 156.8MHz being the designated calling and distress frequency on which all vessels and coast radio stations should listen.

Rather than spell out the actual frequency, the channels used on the marine VHF band are numbered for easy reference from 1 to 88 with the calling and distress frequency being channel 16. These marine band channels are internationally recognised but local radios will have prescribed working frequencies which can be found in almanacs and guides and in some cases are shown on charts. By having numbered frequencies it is much easier to remember the appropriate channels. Switching channels is usually simply a matter punching the appropriate buttons on the channel selector panel.

With modern VHF radio the operation of the radio has been greatly simplified. After switching on it is usually just a simple matter of adjusting the volume and selecting the appropriate channel. These radios can be equipped with a telephone type of handset which incorporates a transmit/receive switch. A smaller palm microphone is sometimes used and in both cases a loudspeaker is fitted to the set so that a listening watch can be maintained.

VHF radios can be operated in the simplex and duplex mode if suitably equipped. Simplex means that only one party in a two-way exchange can talk at one time. At the end of talking he says 'over' and it is the turn of the other party to talk. Conversation of this kind takes a bit of getting used to, but is necessary because the radio cannot transmit and receive simultaneously. Simplex working is the most common form of VHF use; duplex working being mainly used for telephone links. Duplex working uses two channels, one to transmit and one to receive, but these are normally selected automatically through a single channel number. Certain of the higher number channels have been allocated for duplex working.

VHF radio provides slightly greater than line-of-sight communications. This means that the antenna of the transmitting radio must be 'visible' to the receiving aerial without the curvature of the earth, or mountains getting in the way. The transmitted signal follows this curvature very slightly which is why you get a bit more than the direct line-of-sight. If you want maximum range it is essential for the antenna to be as high as possible and on sailing yachts it should have priority at the masthead.

Boat-to-boat range will be limited because of comparatively low antenna heights, whilst communications to the shore will generally benefit from the relatively high antenna of most shore stations. Boat-to-boat links may only be possible over 10-15 miles whilst shore links can sometimes be maintained up to 60-70 miles in good conditions although 40 miles is probably a more realistic figure.

The marine band UHF radio should be regarded as the primary radio communications system for yachts sailing close to land. Channel 16 is fully monitored by Coast Guard and other shore stations for emergency calls and a yacht can be sure of getting a response to a call provided it is in range. The limited range of VHF is a mixed blessing because it will restrict your ability to communicate as you get further offshore but at the same time it cuts down interference and congestion. This limited range allows the same frequencies to be used in different areas without conflict.

CB radios also operate on the VHF frequencies and can provide a communications link. CB radios tend to be cheaper than the marine band radios and there is a temptation to install them as an alternative to the marine band radio. CB radios will provide a link with other vessels and with matching radios on shore, but such links are less reliable and safe and cannot be used to make telephone calls into the land system.

The CB radio frequencies are not monitored in the same way as the marine band, although attitudes in this respect are changing and some authorities monitor designated frequencies. With an urgent or distress message you have to rely on a certain element of luck if you transmit on CB frequencies. Whilst you can probably guarantee that someone is listening out, you cannot guarantee that they will take the necessary action on your behalf. The most useful role for CB afloat is in being able to bypass the telephone system and talk directly with private radios on shore. The use of marine band transmitters on shore is limited to approved users and private direct links are very much frowned upon.

Yachtsmen in many parts of the world now have a new radio link on VHF frequencies which allows them to make direct automatic telephone calls through the land telephone system. This is cellular radio, which cuts out the need to make contact through an operator and reduces delays. With cellular radio, the yacht user simply dials a code and the required number and is connected. The radio signal from the yacht passes to an antenna on shore and if the yacht moves out of range of one shore transmitter, the link is automatically passed to the next one. The whole system is automatic and computer controlled and tailor-made for the yachtsman who needs to keep in touch. In many cases the on-board telephone unit is portable and can be used equally well in a vehicle if suitable antenna can be connected. Cellular radio is designed primarily as a shore-based system, so has limited coverage in coastal waters, usually up to about 20 miles offshore.

With the marine coverage being only a secondary consideration in many cellular radio systems, the coverage may not always be reliable, particularly near areas of high land.

MF-SSB Radios

MF-SSB radios operating on the medium frequencies (MF) represent the next step up in marine communications. This type of equipment was the mainstay of yacht communications before VHF radio came on the scene and its use was very limited because the equipment was large, power hungry and not very reliable at sea. Times have changed and the modern MF-SSB radio is a compact piece of equipment, rivalling the VHF radio in size and offering good reliability.

The attraction of using MF-SSB is its extended range over which it can provide reliable communication with the shore. This can be up to 200 miles in good conditions but 100 to 150 miles would be more reliable coverage. For most yachtsmen this is more than adequate and an MF radio could meet all the yachtsman's requirements in terms of range. It is this very range, however, which also limits the use of MF radio because it leads to congestion on the available channels and much less freedom in the available links with the shore. Most communications with the shore on the MF frequencies have to go through designated shore stations.

The 2MHz band is used for MF-SSB transmissions with 2182KHz being the calling and distress frequencies. Like channel 16 on VHF this is an internationally recognised frequency and other frequencies are designated for simplex and duplex working, as well as for ship-to-ship calling. Channels are sometimes designated by number, but more usually by the actual frequency.

The modern type of SSB MF radio which can meet most radio communications requirements for coastal passage making.

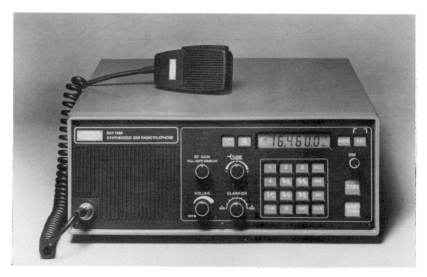

The earlier MF-SSB receivers required a degree of manual tuning to operate successfully, but modern radios of this type use crystal-controlled frequencies which allow push-button channel changing and make operation much more simple and precise. A micro-processor control system is used in many of these radios to automate the tuning process and to keep the radio operating at its optimum performance.

MF-SSB radios require a larger antenna system than that required for VHF. On sailing yachts the backstay can be used as the antenna if it is suitably insulated. The alternative for powerboats is a large whip antenna but whichever type is used both the antenna and its associated ground plane have to be carefully installed to get good results. The operation and installation of an MF-SSB radio requires more care than with VHF but if you are going offshore and want to maintain contact then the MF radio is essential. The power output of a normal yacht MF radio is in the order of 150 watts. With modern technology, it is possible to combine the MF radio with HF in one compact unit to give coverage over a much wider frequency range. This type of radio would give wide ocean coverage but it is essential to have an antenna and its associated tuning system capable of handling this wide frequency range. Modern tuners are automatic so that switching frequencies can be a simple push-button operation.

HF Radio and Satellite Communications

For the ocean sailor requiring a longer range capability from his radio, the choice lies between HF-SSB and satellite communications. HF-SSB is the traditional system using frequencies in 4 to 22MHz band. The radios used for HF are fairly large if a reasonable power output of around 400 watts is required but modern developments allow the control panel to be separated from the main equipment which can simplify the installation. Equipment like this is mainly for the larger yacht unless there is a pressing need for communications in ocean waters. The compact combined radios working on MF and HF can, however, be a useful low-powered substitute.

HF radio transmissions make use of the reflecting properties of the ionosphere to extend the transmission range. The transmitted signal bounces between the earth's surface and the ionosphere as it travels round the globe and this can give long range coverage up to 6000 miles. Transmission and reception can suffer from the problem that the height of the ionosphere is not constant, ranging from 30 to 300 miles above the earth's surface. The height and intensity of this reflecting layer varies on a daily and seasonal basis as well as with other factors and this makes the frequency selected

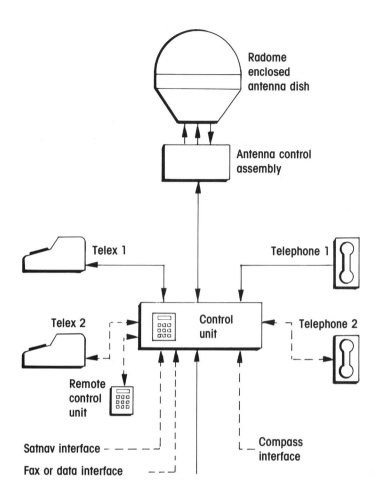

Radome enclosed antenna dish

Antenna control assembly

Telex 1

Telephone 1

Telex 2

Control unit

Telephone 2

Remote control unit

Satnav interface

Compass interface

Fax or data interface

The components of an on board satellite communications package. Dotted lines indicate optional equipment.

critical to obtaining good communications. Blank areas can occur due to the signal skipping and these blank zones are usually between 50 and 750 miles from the transmitting station.

From this it becomes apparent that the operating frequency will have to be selected to match the conditions and position. Much of this is determined by working schedules in different parts of the world and this complicates the operating procedures. HF radio is primarily for making telephone and telex links and once established these can be quite satisfactory, but an element of patience is needed to make the connection. Links are made through shore stations and thence to the land telephone system. Because of the range requirements higher transmitted power is needed and the antenna requirements become more critical.

For reliable communictions on a worldwide basis, HF-SSB has many limitations and it was this which provided the incentive for the development of satellite communications (satcom) for use by ships. Satcom ground stations on shore have direct links with satellites through large dish antenna. The satellites remain fairly stationary over the earth's surface and there are three main satellites serving the Atlantic, Pacific and Indian oceans. These satellites link with small steerable dish antennae on board vessels. This onboard antenna has to have a rapid response rate to keep the dish pointing at the satellite irrespective of the vessel's position and movement. The aim is to provide a high quality radio link between the vessel and the ground station from where the link goes into the land telephone system.

The whole telephone and telex link with satcom is automatic. The required code and number is dialled either way and the system operates in a very similar manner to a land telephone. The weak link in the chain is the onboard steerable antenna which at the present state of development has a diameter of at least 1 metre and a response rate which is not fast enough to cope with the movement of small yachts. The antenna size is getting smaller and a new generation of higher powered satellites will help to reduce the size still further, but at present a user of satcom has to find space on board for a dome about 2 metres high and 1.2 metres in diameter. This rules out satcom for all but the largest yachts at present, but rapid developments are taking place and we may well see satcom being used to meet all communications requirements in the not too distant future. Meanwhile the HF-SSB is the only method of communications for most yachts venturing over 200 miles offshore. The HF radio offers cheaper telephone links than those available through satcom and the equipment itself is much cheaper even if the quality of the link and its convenience are not so good.

A waterproof portable VHF radio which can be a useful addition to any yacht's inventory and can play a major role in emergency situations.

Portable Radios

With the advent of electronic miniaturisation, portable VHF radios have been developed and these can be very useful. These handheld units are battery powered, have a built in antenna and some units on the market are waterproof. This waterproofing is a great advantage at sea and is generally worth the extra cost. It allows the radio to be used in the cockpit when entering harbour irrespective of the conditions, but one of the main attractions of these portable radios is in an emergency.

Sailing yachts are frequently dismasted. This usually brings down the antenna just at a time when you need help and the portable radio can be a useful back-up. If things get really bad and you have to abandon your yacht for the life-raft, then the portable still enables you to maintain the essential link with rescuers. In more routine ways the portable can also be useful if you use a tender. Sending the portable away in the tender enables you to maintain contact with your crew or the kids, all of which can bring peace of mind or save time.

Normally such a portable would operate on selected frequencies on the marine VHF band but here you are limited to using the portable when afloat. The authorities will not thank you if you call up your crew in the supermarket to order more bread, although a CB portable could be used for this purpose. Marine VHF is reserved for marine matters and this should be respected.

Telex and Navtex

Telex communications are assuming increasing importance and can be a useful way of passing messages without the need for the called party to be in attendance. The use of telex is probably mainly valuable to those who have to remain in business contact whilst out at sea and it can operate through any on-board radio which is equipped to make telephone calls provided provision has been made for a telex interface. A keyboard and usually a video display for composing and printing messages is needed so that this facility is normally reserved for the larger yacht.

Area planned for the worldwide coverage of the Navtex warning and weather forecast system.

Portable personal computers provide a new approach to telex. One system developed along these lines can be linked to a radio set to send and receive telex messages. The computer can also be used for a variety of other purposes. Telex is only one of the software programmes. Another one allows the computer to decode and print out weatherfax charts. In this way we are seeing the development of the communications computer which will effectively control the operation of one or more radios, switching on to receive weather and other messages and even transmitting at specified times.

A form of telex which has application for all yachts is Navtex. This is in effect a one-way telex system which allows automatic communication on a fixed frequency between a shore station and the fitted vessel. Any messages transmitted are automatically printed out without any action necessary on board except switching on.

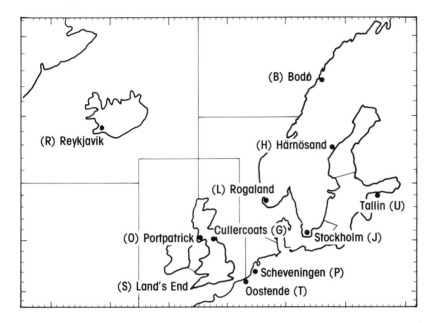

Transmitting stations and areas of the European Navtex system.

A Navtex receiver which automatically receives and prints out weather forecasts and emergency messages.

Navtex is used for transmitting weather forecasts, gale warnings, distress messages and navigation warnings. With a Navtex receiver on board, the yachtsman knows that he is getting all the important messages he should have without the need to keep a constant radio watch. At the time of writing, the Navtex transmissions cover the whole of Northern Europe and parts of the USA, the latter on an experimental basis, but the aim is to develop the system worldwide to provide a coastal warning system which would complement an ocean system operating through satcom. To avoid receiving a lot of unnecessary information, the user can be selective about the areas and type of information being received. Distress messages, however, cannot be removed and sound an alarm on receipt. Navtex receivers have to conform to stringent ship requirements and are not particularly cheap at present, but cost is likely to reduce as the market grows.

EPIRBs and Safety

Instead of shouting for help over the radio when you are in trouble, the Emergency Position Indicating Radio Beacon (EPIRB) can do the job automatically for you. As EPIRBs come in many shapes or forms and there are new systems under development the optimum system is under debate. Much will depend on the area of operation of the vessel and most yachtsmen are going to be interested in systems suitable for coastal rather than ocean waters.

The simplest type of EPIRB transmits a signal when activated manually. This distinctive signal is picked up on shore or by other vessels or aircraft and the rescue services can home in on it.

EPIRBS operating on 123.5 and 243 MHz can be picked up by aircraft and satellites. Satellites can also give an approximate position. Rescue helicopters and aircraft can also home in on the signals.

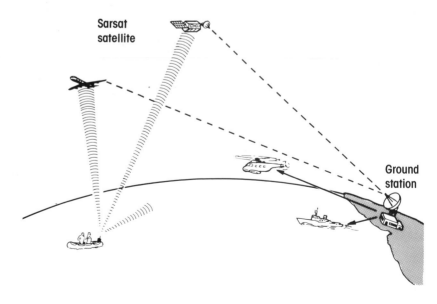

Sarsat satellite

Ground station

Originally EPIRBs operated on medium frequencies, generally on 2182kHz which was the marine calling and distress frequency. Because of the low transmitter power and interference on these frequencies, these distress beacons were never very successful and an alternative was the marine VHF band. Here the range was very limited mainly because of low antenna height and a switch was made to using the aircraft distress frequencies of 121.5 and 243MHz. These frequencies were restricted entirely to aircraft use at one time, and the use of these frequencies for marine distress beacons was illegal until fairly recently. Now these frequencies are available for marine distress beacons they are becoming more widely used and there are several on the market today. The attraction of the aircraft frequencies is that the antenna height on overflying aircraft is high and this can greatly increase the range of detection of the distress signal.

Both these marine and aircraft frequency distress beacons, however, are comparatively short range units. The attraction of developing a satellite system for these distress beacons is that such a system would operate on a worldwide basis and signals could be received by the satellite no matter where the yacht was in trouble. Once received by the satellite, the signal could then be amplified and transmitted down to a shore station so that suitable rescue action cold be initiated.

Two satellite systems have been proposed, and one is currently in operation. This operational system is the SARSAT-COSPAS

Areas of direct satellite coverage with the Sarsat-Cospas system when the satellite can link the beacon signal directly to a ground station. In other areas, the satellite stores the information for transmission when linked to a ground station.

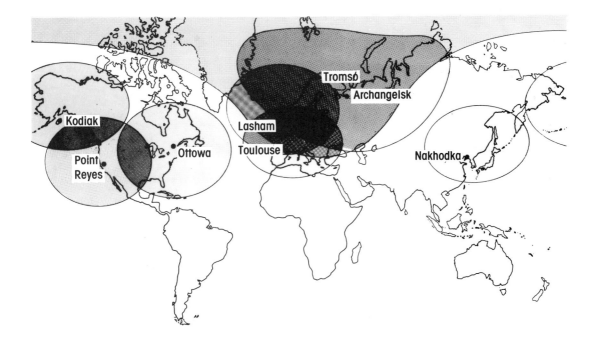

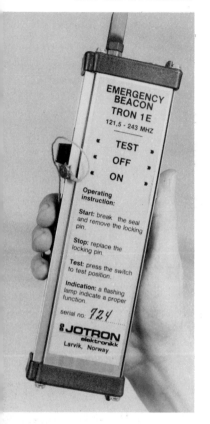

An EPIRB operating on the two aircraft emergency frequencies of 121.5 and 243 MHz. Even smaller pocket sized units are available.

project, which comprises four satellites in a polar orbit. The COSPAS part of this project is a Soviet satellite and this monitors both 121.5MHz and 400.025MHz. The SARSAT part of the system comprises three satellites in polar orbit which will be part of the Tiros-N weather satellites. This part of the project is being funded mainly by the USA, Canada, and France and because the 121.5MHz signals are very weak at the 600 mile height of these satellites, they will only monitor the 400.025 frequency.

This system would appear to meet most of the requirements of a worldwide system and it will be able to locate a distress beacon anywhere in the world with an accuracy of between 1 and 6 miles. A flaw, however, in this system is that there can be a delay of up to three hours in the reception of a distress signal because the satellite pattern does not give complete coverage all the time. This inadequacy could be solved by using more satellites but this would be very costly if dedicated satellites were used, and an alternative system which will use the INMARSAT satellite communications system is under development.

In contrast to the polar orbit of the SARSAT-COSPAS system, the INMARSAT system uses geo-stationary satellites which stay in a fixed position above the earth's surface. The position of these three satellites has been designed to give worldwide coverage between latitudes 75 North and 75 South.

Ideally these two satellite systems would be combined to provide one all-embracing system but here again there are problems because the INMARSAT satellites are located a long way from the earth's surface and the emergency system planned for these satellites will operate at a different frequency, 1.6GHz.

The EPIRBs for use with the INMARSAT system would be linked to an electronic position finding system when on board so that they would have a continuously updated position until

Coverage provided by the three satellites of the Inmarsat system. Two satellites operate in each region and link with the appropriate ground stations.

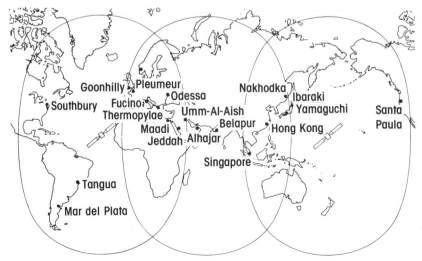

activated, which would help locations. These EPIRBs would be both quite large and expensive and would only be justified for use on yachts on ocean passages.

The choice of which EPIRB system is difficult, but the best solution at present would seem to be the 121.5MHz frequency, provided that your sailing is done in an area where a reasonable number of aircraft are flying overhead. It must be remembered that these EPIRBs only indicate distress and not where it has occurred which may lead to a considerable time lapse between activating the signal and help arriving. There is also no voice capability on these EPIRBs so that you have no way of knowing if your signal has been heard.

EPIRBs have a value as a safety aid, but a great deal more development is required before they provide the complete answer. There has been a considerable problem with false alarms from EPIRBs mainly due to these units being triggered when in storage or being tampered with by unauthorised people. These false alarms are reaching a worrying level and if you carry an EPIRB you have a responsibility to look after it both for your own sake and for that of others who may need to send out an emergency signal for real.

Satellite links will be the way ahead in future for emergency signals because there will be no limitations on the coverage. In the meantime, your radio should be considered as the first line of defence in an emergency, backed up by a waterproof portable and the EPIRB. For rescue to be effected, the rescuers need to know where you are, what you are and what the problem is. The radio can give all three answers, the EPIRB in its present form, only one or two.

Weatherfax and Satellite Pictures

The ability to give vessels at sea important weather information has led to the development of specialised equipment. In the USA continuous weather information is broadcast on dedicated channels and the yachtsman should ensure that these frequencies are available on board. In Europe weather information tends to be passed at specific times over channels used for other purposes. To get a good picture of the weather pattern a yachtsman may need to take information from several sources. A radio receiver is often carried on board to receive these weather messages and it is now possible to get receivers which incorporate a timer and tape recorder allowing the receiver to be programmed to receive and record the weather information automatically at selected times.

Even with the best endeavours of the authorities, a weather report is out of date when received. With changing weather

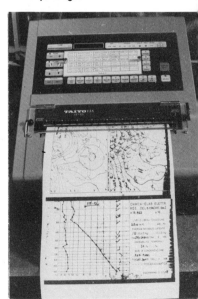

A facsimile receiver which can produce weather, ice, sea state and temperature charts. Ocean going yachts use these as one of the few reliable sources of weather information on ocean passages.

**A typical marine band
VHF radio which forms
the backbone on yacht
communication systems
today.**

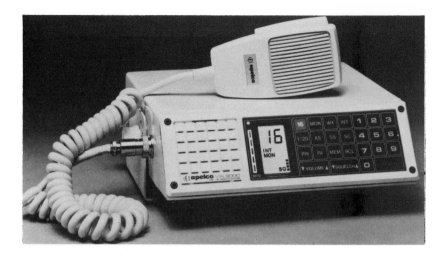

patterns, a yachtsman needs to relate the pattern to prevailing
conditions to be able to make a full assessment of what the weather
may do and this is where the weatherfax comes in useful. The size
and cost of a fax machine may rule it out for all but the serious or
offshore yachtsmen but both size and cost are coming down and
this may be considered essential equipment for the serious
sailor.

The weatherfax is essentially a radio receiver which can pick up
coded signals. When these are translated electronically, they can
be used to draw the weather chart on the printer incorporated into
the weatherfax. The printed map can range in size from 6 to 8
inches across and the operation of the fax receiver is largely
automatic once the appropriate frequency has been selected.
Coded signals in the transmission will set the printer going.
Crystal tuning is often used to simplify operation, but this may
limit the number of stations from which charts can be received.

Far more information is available on a weather chart than can be
presented in a weather forecast. Different charts can show past,
present and anticipated weather patterns to build up a picture,
whilst other charts can show weather fronts and highs and lows,
cloud patterns and storm development, surface winds, wave
analysis, ocean currents, sea temperature and ice formations.

The Navtex system is a poor substitute for the vast amount of
information available by weatherfax, but it is one way of receiving
forecasts automatically. The Navtex forecasts, however, will
inevitably be general in nature. Quite detailed weather forecasts
for ocean areas are also broadcast in Morse Code and receivers are
now available which can translate the Morse Code automatically
and print out the message. The ocean yachtsman should consider
both this and the weatherfax whilst the coastal inshore yachtsman
is likely to rely on broadcast messages as these will probably give

him as much information as he needs. The racing yachtsman may opt for the weatherfax, because he needs the fullest possible weather information.

Information obtained directly from satellite cameras can produce real-time information about weather patterns and is available on shore. Obtaining the information from some weather satellites requires a directional dish antenna, but two satellites in use broadcast a strong signal which does not require a directional antenna. This information can be received on board. The picture is

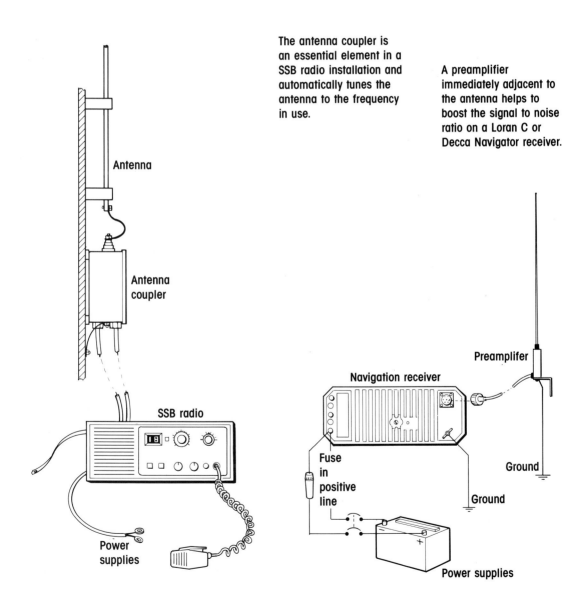

The antenna coupler is an essential element in a SSB radio installation and automatically tunes the antenna to the frequency in use.

A preamplifier immediately adjacent to the antenna helps to boost the signal to noise ratio on a Loran C or Decca Navigator receiver.

Antenna

Antenna coupler

SSB radio

Power supplies

Navigation receiver

Preamplifer

Fuse in positive line

Ground

Ground

Power supplies

displayed on a video screen. The equipment is large and hardly yacht compatible at present, but developments may allow these direct pictures to be available in the future. In the meantime, the best that is available is the satellite picture translated into a weatherfax map.

Antenna

The importance of the antenna in all radio installations cannot be over-emphasised. The best transmitter in the world will not operate satisfactorily unless the power is actually radiated from the antenna. Within the confines of a yacht the various antennae required for different equipment will compete for priority. Most antennae require height and a clear position. On a sailing yacht the masthead is the optimum position, with the aft pulpit rail being a second best. On power yachts, good height cannot be achieved easily but there is generally more space.

Obviously a compromise has to be reached and it is necessary to decide priorities at the different available locations bearing in mind that the electronic position finding equipment will also need to be considered. For a sailing yacht the masthead should be given over to the VHF antenna and the backstay, suitably insulated, can be used as the MF or HF-SSB antenna. This leaves the aft pulpit available for the position finding equipment, but the backstay antenna could cause interference. On a powerboat, a whip antenna will probably be used for the MF or HF and here the various antennae can be spaced out more to reduce interference.

With each piece of equipment, whether radio or position finding, requiring its own antenna, the limitations on what can be installed is likely to be determined by the space for antennae. Because of this, dual purpose antennae are attractive and manufacturers are looking at ways in which separate antennae can be combined. The problem of the antenna should be the primary consideration when looking for new equipment and the radio antennae are the most critical because they radiate power rather than being passive receivers. It is wise to get professional advice before installing an MF or an HF antenna.

As the radio plays an important role in safety and the mast supports most of the antennae on a sailing yacht, the question of an emergency antenna should be considered. Dismasting is likely to be one cause of an emergency. Whilst the portable radio already described can overcome this problem, an alternative is to have an emergency antenna which can be clipped to a suitable point with the lead plugged into the radio. With MF or HF the problem is more difficult, but a suitably insulated wire strung up would give some form of transmission although at much reduced output.

An electronic security system for yachts. The control box can be linked to a number of sensors to cover engine alarms, gas, bilge water, battery condition and intruder alarms. Shown here is the infra-red sensing device to detect intruders. The unit can be programmed as required and can be linked to audio and/or visual alarms.

12 Safety, security and even television

The main areas of yachts electronics have already been covered in this book but there are other aspects. On power yachts, the use of electronics to monitor engine performance and fuel consumption will be an area of growing interest and domestic electronics such as TV and Hi-Fi are used on yachts. Electronics are adding to safety in a variety of ways apart from the obvious benefits of radio communications.

Like other on-board electronic systems the approach in these areas has been piecemeal up to now. The increasing complexity of the systems being developed, particularly for safety, security and engine monitoring point the way towards the use of fully integrated systems which will present the yachtsman with a full status picture of all the systems on board. Yachtsmen are looking more and more to have all the comforts and security of home life on board their yachts and the development and installation of suitable electronic systems presents a challenge to manufacturers. The conditions on board are very different from the home and normal domestic equipment doesn't always make a happy transition even if the space and power supplies are available to support it.

TV, Radio and Hi-Fi

TV and radio can make the transfer to yacht use quite happily, because both have been well developed in portable form to stand vibration and rough usage. Naturally they will not stand up to water, but the cabin on board most yachts is dry. Portable TV and radio are best suited to yacht use, partly because they are constructed ruggedly, but also because the power requirements can be compatible with the low voltage on board, and the size of the equipment is more in tune with the space available. It is important to provide secure stowages for radios and TV because this equipment is designed to stand alone and it is all too easy to forget to stow it before going to sea.

The critical part in getting any TV receiver to operate on board a yacht is the antenna. Normal TV antennae are made directional to get the strongest signal to the receiver. A directional antenna is not practical on a yacht as it is continually changing heading and so special omni-directional antennae have been developed for this purpose. With such antennae, there will be a loss of signal strength compared with a directional antenna, but this is compensated for to a degree for having a pre-amplifier incorporated into the antenna unit to boost the signal. The TV antenna should be mounted as high as possible and if you only use the set in harbour then a portable antenna is best. This system would also be a good precaution against TV interference with a Loran C receiver, where the TV can radiate signals which can reduce the sensitivity of the Loran signals.

Domestic Hi-Fi equipment is really unsuited for use on yachts, but fortunately the equipment provided for car use is ideal both in terms of voltage and space requirements. It is designed to stand up to movement and for building in so that it is almost tailor-made for the job. None of the car Hi-Fi will stand up to water so don't put the speakers in the cockpit, although special speakers are now available designed for yacht use. Loud music outside, however can quickly lose friends in a marina, so music is best restricted to inside installations.

Engine Monitoring and Fuel Meters

Engine monitoring systems are something of a no-man's land. Some engine manufacturers make them available as options with

The components of a fuel consumption system for a diesel engine using a return reservoir.

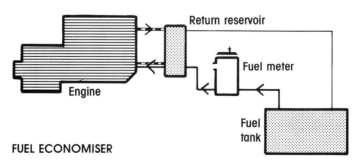

FUEL ECONOMISER

their engines, whilst there seems a reluctance amongst electronics manufacturers to get involved in this area probably because of the diversity of fittings and fixtures which would have to be supplied to make the equipment suitable for the wide range of engines on the market. This equipment, however, is being slowly developed adn we may well see a situation where an electronics company produces the basic equipment and each engine manufacturer provides the measuring transducers to adapt the equipment to its engines, with the marketing being carried out by the engine people.

A sophisticated fuel consumption system which takes into account factors such as propeller slip and trim. Units such as this can only be justified on larger motor yachts but smaller units are under development. Fully computerised engine monitoring units will be developed for yachts.

Engine monitoring can do a great deal more than the simple gauges currently used to monitor engine operating conditions. In addition to displaying readings of important engine parameters, both high and low alarms can be built in to give warning of a malfunction. These alarms can be quite subtle and instead of setting a threshold reading to trigger the alarm they could also give warning if a reading started to rise or fall rapidly. In this way early warning could be given of any fault arising so that corrective action could prevent major damage. Automatic shutdown could be built in, although most yachtsmen would prefer to maintain manual control of this.

Another feature which can be built into engine monitoring is the recording of historical data. If a reading of each parameter is taken say, once every hour of running and then displayed in relation to other readings, any gradual deterioration would become apparent and allow corrective action to be taken before major problems arise. If log readings are added to the inputs, the speed through the water can be related to the engine performance so that any reduction in performance through propeller damage or bottom fouling will become apparent.

Fuel monitoring equipment can be extended in the same way. In its simplest form a fuel monitor shows the rate at which fuel is being consumed in units per hour. Add in a log input and the gallons per mile (through the water) can be obtained. When this is related to rpm, any deterioration in performance will become apparent. The fuel meter can also be linked into the position finding equipment and fuel tank gauges and the amount of fuel on board at the end of the voyage can be projected. In this way the powerboat man can have a complete picture of his engine and fuel system and feel much more in control of the situation. Comprehensive systems of this type for yacht use are in their early stages of development but they are already available for larger commercial vessels so that suitable equipment for the yacht market is really a question of demand rather than any difficult technical problems.

Security and Alarm Systems

A yacht left at a marina or on a mooring can be exposed to many risks. Intruders are one problem, and both fire and flooding could also pose a threat to security. Electronic systems can help to give warning of these problems even if they can't engineer a solution and are worth considering if you want to sleep soundly at night away from your yacht. Insurance companies might also take kindly to the installation by reducing premiums.

The various areas on a yacht which can benefit from theft or intruder protection. Different types of sensor will be required for different tasks.

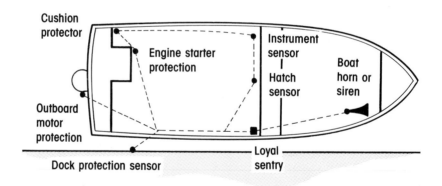

The electronics used to give warning about intruders and fire are similar to those used in houses. Pressure switches under mats are one way of warning against intruders and the doors and hatches can be covered with various types of alarm. As these are all likely to be powered from the yacht's battery, this should be located in a secure place so that it can't be isolated by the intruder.

Fire detectors can work by detecting smoke, flame or a rise in temperature. The smoke detector is probably the best of the three for a yacht left unattended as it will give the earliest warning of a problem. Once flames are detected it is probably too late to salvage very much of the situation. Smoke detectors are not much use with a crew of smokers on board.

Bilge alarms give warning of high water levels in the bilges which can result if a water hose breaks unexpectedly or if another yacht collides. The normal electric bilge pump with float switch will only take care of small amounts of leakage.

The type of alarm used for all of these systems will depend on the circumstances. A flashing light may be appropriate or a siren or other loud noise could be used. It all depends on whose attention you are trying to attract or who you are trying to frighten off. A light would have to be on deck to be effective and could easily be disabled by an intruder so on balance a loud noise is probably best. A remote indicator in the marina office linked by cable or radio is another possibility but becomes expensive.

Petrol engines or gas bottles for cooking or heating can cause further problems. Leaks in either of these systems can create an explosive mixture in the bilges and you should have a warning system to indicate the problem. A number of types are on the market, the main difference being in the way they indicate the problem. The time when a build up of gas is most likely is after the boat has been left for a while or after refuelling. The indicator system should be automatic and located in a position where you will see it before you start pressing switches. One indicator at the engine starting position and one down below is an adequate safeguard and bright lights are best used for such systems. The gas detectors should be placed low down in the bilges where the gas will first collect because it is heavier than air. Separate detectors will be necessary if the bilges are divided.

In the move towards electronic integration it is becoming fashionable for all these safety and security systems to be linked into one control panel. This can reduce the overall cost of a comprehensive system and it makes it much more likely that you will check out the panel at regular intervals. A security system is only useful if it continues to function at all times. Reliability is important and the more sophisticated units on the market have a self testing feature to ensure that the system is functioning correctly.

Man Overboard Alarms

One of the more serious situations facing yachtsmen is a man overboard. Firstly there is the problem of actually knowing when a crew member is overboard and time can be important here in helping with the second problem which is actually locating the person. Several electronic devices have been developed to help in this difficult situation.

The most critical time is when a crew member is on deck alone. If he goes overboard he may not be missed for some time. Small water-activated transmitters are available. The transmitter is carried in a pocket so that it is quickly immersed if the user falls overboard. The link to the onboard monitor can be by radio or sound signal and the alarm can be a sound signal or it can link directly to the engine to shut it off. The sound alarm is adequate for most purposes because the engine is needed to turn the yacht round to pick the person up.

A more logical link would be with the position finding equipment in order to fix the position. Many position finding receivers are equipped with a man-overboard override which can be linked to a cockpit push button. Pressing this button freezes the position where the crew member went overboard and with the good repeatable accuracy of these systems it should be fairly easy to work the yacht back close to the crew member in the water.

Another electronic man-overboard aid is found on some autopilots. Most yachtsmen know that to turn the yacht back on to its reciprocal track is not just a matter of putting the helm hard over. This would take you back on a parallel track and the Williamson Turn is the correct procedure involving putting the helm hard over one way, allowing a 60 degree swing before putting the helm hard over the other way. Some of the more sophisticated autopilots with micro-processor control have this type of turn programmed in so that by simply hitting the man overboard button the yacht is returned to a course down its original track along which the man overboard should lie. Such a system is really only applicable to yachts under power. Sail handling could compromise such a manoeuvre even if the wind did allow the yacht to sail on the desired track. Here the position fix on the position finding equipment is the answer, backed up by the personal transmitter if this is felt desirable.

If a waterproof portable VHF radio is carried on board, any crew member on deck alone should have it to make contact in case he fell overboard. It is much easier for the person in the water to see the yacht than vice-versa, so that he could direct it towards him, assuming that he is conscious and competent.

13 Installation and power supplies

As the range of electronic equipment used on board yachts grows, installing the equipment and meeting the power requirements can present considerable problems. Not only can equipment and antennae interfere with each other, but they can also compromise the operation of compasses and other equipment. Electronics can be non-waterproof, splashproof or fully waterproof and the installation must take into account the protection required for each piece of equipment. Bear in mind that when you come in from the cockpit, you may be dripping with water which will not mix happily with the electronic circuits.

Many problems stem from the fact that even modern yachts are rarely designed with the installation of electronics in mind and that electronics manufacturers have not yet got around to the idea of the standardisation of electronic packages and the production of electronics equipment in a modular form. Current equipment comes in a wide variety of shapes and sizes, all designed for independent installation and the problems mount.

The yachtsman is not immune from criticism because he will go to a number of manufacturers when he purchases equipment for his yacht and will probably buy the equipment piecemeal without any overall plan. This is hardly surprising. The rapid developments in yacht electronics make it difficult to anticipate

The wide variety of electronic packages makes it difficult to achieve a tidy installation. Separating controls from displays can help as in the case of this remote control radar.

what will be on board in, say, five years time, and what the size of the electronic packages will be.

Things are likely to get better. As we move towards integrated electronics it seems probable that the information displays will be separated from the 'box-of-tricks' which produces the information. This is already happening with radar where on some versions the control panel and the display are separated. With fully integrated electronics there may be a central VDU and control panel with the remainder of the electronics tucked away out of sight.

This approach would help installation, but in the meantime the yacht owner is faced with finding space for a number of odd shaped pieces of equipment and with a variety of associated antenna and transducers all of which may conflict in some way. The available space is rarely sufficient to enable the optimum layout to be achieved and a great deal of thought will be necessary to get the best out of the equipment.

There will be certain key positions in the yacht where the important equipment should be located. Power and sailing yachts have different requirements and they will be studied individually.

Power Yachts

Electronic equipment on power craft can generally be protected from the elements so there is little requirement for water or splashproof equipment. The exception will be the flying bridge or the open steering position found on some very fast craft. Here there is a very definite need for equipment which will not give in when spray or rain is flying about. Splashproof equipment will generally be adequate if the equipment is kept covered and not left exposed all winter.

The flying bridge will generally need a compass and an echo sounder, with the remainder of the equipment stowed safely under cover at the main steering position. A VHF radio of either the portable or waterproof type could also be an advantage outside. Inside, the radios and position finding equipment can be located at the chart table and this arrangement leaves more space at the steering position. Also there will be less magnetic compass interference.

The radar presents something of a dilemma. For general use the radar can be happily placed where the helmsman can use it. In clear weather a quick glance can show the layout of the coastline or other navigation features, but in poor visibility the radar needs a lot more concentration and should fully occupy one crew member. It therefore needs to be placed where it can be used comfortably for long periods and where it will not interfere with the helmsman. In practice these two ideals are rarely met and the compromise position does not allow the radar to be used to its best. A swivel and clamp mounting can combine both requirements, allowing the radar to be moved, but with limited space available, and power yachts being used mainly in fine weather, the position by the helmsman is usually favourite. The modern daylight viewing radars give better flexibility for locating the radar but they should not be placed in direct sunlight. The detachable control panel also helps with installation.

When a power yacht has two steering positions it is often possible to have secondary monitors for much of the main equipment. This is cheaper than having duplicate installations and it is much easier to make the monitors waterproof because they have few control knobs. If separate pieces of equipment are fitted at each steering position the yacht has an element of redundancy in the equipment, although the cost will obviously be higher.

Most electronic equipment has lights of one sort or another, either from the information panel or in the form of warning lights. At night these can cause considerable interference with the visibility through the wheelhouse windows unless the installation has been carried out to minimise the effect. A lot of yacht electronic equipment has a dimming system for night use, but the display panels should not reflect into sloping wheelhouse windows or distract from the direct vision ahead. Before making a final choice of position for equipment it should be tested in the selected position at night to see just what the effect is.

On a power yacht the electrical requirements for the electronics should present little problem, although the circuit system should be carefully thought out to reduce the electrical surges and peaks which can harm sensitive electronics. Each piece of equipment should operate off a separate circuit with duplex wiring for the connection. The electrical system should be installed with a number of spare circuits for additional equipment to be added later and each circuit should have a separate switch or circuit breaker.

Memory in electronic equipment may be wiped out through a cut or reduction of the input voltage. Most equipment now has the memory protected by a small lithium battery so that waypoint information is not lost, without which problems can occur. The electronics should be on a separate battery to the engine starting battery, otherwise you might find all your nicely programmed waypoints have been wiped off due to the voltage drop when the engine is started.

Interference from a variety of sources can be another problem. Check by switching each electrical unit on in turn, but also try starting the engine and turning the shaft as both of these can create problems when underway. Suppression devices can be fitted to

Sources of interference to the electronics instruments on a yacht. RDF and navigation receivers are the most sensitive.

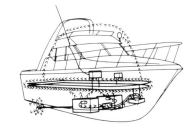

most equipment or alternatively it is possible to fit a main suppressor on the electronic equipment circuits to smooth out the power supply. Although marine electronic equipment is designed to be very tolerant to bad power supplies, you give the equipment a better start in life by sorting out the power supply before it gets to the equipment.

Sailing Yachts

The layout of electronic equipment on a sailing yacht is divided between the cockpit and down below, the latter usually being at the chart table. The cockpit of a sailing yacht tends to be much wetter than the flying bridge of a power yacht, and sailing yachts are often out in far worse weather so only fully waterproof equipment is suitable for cockpit installation. In the past this has generally been limited to the sailing instruments and compass which provide the continuing information required to keep the yacht sailing efficiently. We are now seeing more waterproof equipment being produced for sailing yachts such as autopilots and even radios, but in general the equipment which has control panels and knobs is located down below.

Clear panels in the aft cabin bulkhead can allow equipment to be viewed from the cockpit whilst still keeping it dry. Radar could be installed in this way, but such an installation is less than satisfactory partly due to reflections on the glass or plastic cover, and partly due to the effect of bright sunlight. At night the bright picture can be very distracting.

The most expedient but not ideal place for radar is down below. Here it keeps dry and can be viewed in comfort, but in fog the link between radar and helmsman may not be reliable. The helmsman will always be concerned that the man below is not keeping a continuous watch on the radar.

The logical place for the other electronic equipment is at the chart table and sailing yachts are generally prepared to dedicate more space to this feature than powerboats which makes the use of the equipment easier and more reliable. The layout of the equipment will depend a great deal on personal taste, but instruments with knobs or key pads which require frequent attention should be placed readily to hand. Whilst this chart table should be considered a dry area, it is often necessary to come below with dripping oilskins to operate the equipment so there is some sense in placing it fairly high so that water cannot easily drip on it. If the face of the instrument is angled slightly downwards, any water which does drip on it will run off without doing any harm.

The chart table is usually close to a wet companionway which is another good reason for tucking the equipment up in a well protected area. The VHF radio may need to be operated from either below or in the cockpit and this means mounting it on the deckhead, just inside the companionway. Here it could get very wet, so if the radio is not waterproof, a small drop-down plastic screen can help to keep the worst of the water off.

The comments about wiring and the electrical supply made in the power section are equally applicable to sailing yachts and separating the engine starting and electronics power supply to separate batteries is more important because the engine of a sailing yacht is much more likely to be started at sea.

Antenna, Grounds and Transducers

Any electronic equipment which receives signals or transmits them needs an antenna. An echo sounder performs this function, but uses an underwater transducer and the same could be said for the log. These antennae and transducers are of great importance for the efficient operation of the equipment and they must be positioned and installed correctly. There can be conflicts between antennae and transducers and the placing of these units has to be carefully planned.

The antennae you have to consider belong to the radios, the radar and the position finding equipment. There may also be a need for additional antennae for TV and Navtex. Height is usually a critical factor with any antenna and where practical an antenna should have a clear 'view' around the horizon. Certainly it should not be close to metal in the form of rigging, masts or superstructure.

Two antennae are particularly height critical, the VHF radio and the radar. The masthead should be the place for the VHF antenna and it is possible to combine marine band and CB antenna in one unit to make best use of the available space. Because of its size and weight, the radar antenna is usually mounted on the wheelhouse top or part way up the mast. The smooth contours of the antenna housing need not interfere with the sails on a sailing yacht although they may interrupt the smooth air flow. The radar antenna should not be placed level with and close to the crew standing in the cockpit. The radiated power could cause eye damage.

MF or HF radios demand longer antennae than the short VHF units. These can be either a wire strung between masts, or a whip antenna. The latter is likely to be several metres long depending on the frequency being used. Varying lengths are required for different frequencies and an antenna coupler is used to match the antenna to the frequency without varying the length.

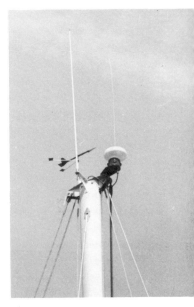

The masthead is the optimum place for many antenna and this is about the maximum which can be accommodated without interference.

One solution to antenna congestion is combining them and here a VHF antenna is integrated with wind sensor transducers.

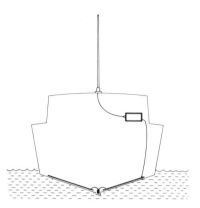

Ground planes for the radio can be placed inside the hull.

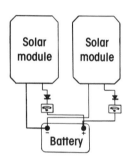

Circuit diagram for two modules in parallel

On a sailing yacht it is common to use the backstay, suitably insulated, as the MF-HF antenna. The high transmission voltages of any radio on these frequencies means that the crew must be protected from accidentally touching the antenna during transmission, which normally means placing the bottom insulator out of reach.

Because they are receive-only equipment, position finding antennae are not so critical in their position requirements. They should be away from rigging and obstructions and the usual position is on a short mast or on the aft pulpit on a sailing yacht and on the wheelhouse top on a power yacht. They should be kept away from transmitting and TV antennae. TV antennae have much the same requirements although height can be more important to avoid interference when moored alongside. For receiving satellite TV it is possible to use portable dish antennae which can be mounted on the deck side and manually directed for harbour use.

Wind sensors need clear air and are almost invariably mounted at the masthead on sailing yachts, cantilevered out forward from the top of the mast. Underwater the log impeller requires a similar good water flow to give accurate readings adn the usual place on a sailing yacht is under the turn of the bilge amidships, with an impeller on each side to ensure that one remains immersed when the yacht is heeled. These should not be placed too close to the keel where the water flow can be disturbed and one of the advantages of the new type of sonic log is that it operates in the good water flow ahead of the keel.

On power yachts the log impeller is usually well aft, particularly on planing craft where the hull sections remain well immersed. Much the same goes for the echo sounder transducer which needs a flow of solid water across its face. Any air bubbles introduce unreliable readings and twin transducers are fitted to many sailing yachts. On planing power yachts, both log and echo sounder transducer can be mounted on the transom and special transducers for this are made by some manufacturers.

Loran and Decca Navigator antennae require good grounding to operate efficiently and reduce interference. This grounding must connect directly to the sea water and is best achieved by linking the earth terminal to a copper plate attached to the outside of the hull. Reasonable results can often be obtained by linking the ground wire to the engine or gearbox provided there is a direct metal link to the propeller, but this is not a necessarily reliable system.

MF and HF antennae also require a good grounding to operate at maximum efficiency. This presents no problem on metal yachts and on sailing yachts the keel sould be used, even though it may be encapsulated in fibreglass. An alternative is to embed metal mesh into the hull laminate on each side of the keel, but the outside copper plate is the best system of all as it serves every requirement. It is the only ground which will provide protection from lightning strike and for this it must be linked to a metal spike on the masthead by a wide copper strip.

Power Supplies

Except for radios when they are transmitting, the power requirements for electronic equipment are not very high. Certainly they should be well within the capabilities of the average alternator and battery system to meet when the engine is running. Shore supplies in the marina are usually available to meet any requirement and with a suitable charger system, can be used to keep the yacht's batteries up to scratch. The problems of electrical supply only become acute when under sail and there are a number of different systems available to provide electrical power both underway and in harbour when the engine is not running.

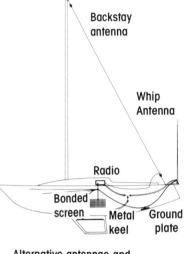

Alternative antennae and grounding systems for an SSB radio.

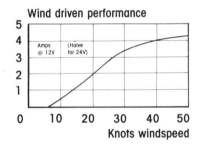 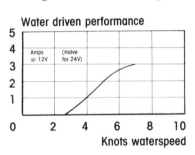

The amount of electrical power which can be generated from typical wind and water powered generators related to the wind or water speed.

Wind generators take the form of a small multi-bladed windmill and will operate both at sea and in harbour. They have to be mounted on a short pole mast to keep them clear of the deck as there is no protection around the blades. Output from these generators is usually between 5 and 10 amps which is adequate to meet the electronic and navigation light requirements of a sailing yacht but these windmills are intrusive and not every yachtsman is going to put up with the drag they create.

Less obstructive but still creating a drag are the 'water-mills', a propeller which revolves through the motion of the boat through the water and which is linked to an alternator. There are two types, one which is towed astern on a special rope like a towed log, and the shaft generator which uses the yacht's propeller taken out of gear and linked to an alternator with a belt drive. The latter type can produce power equivalent to the engine alternator, but you have to pay the penalty in the slowing down of the boat. Both wind and water generators are going to be almost ineffective in light

A full array of navigation and communications electronics on board a trans-ocean racing yacht. In addition to planning the interior layout and power supplies very carefully, particular attention needs to be paid to the location of the various antenna.

winds and with the shaft generator you must keep the stern tube lubricated and ensure that the gearbox is designed to operate for long periods in neutral.

Finally you can use the sun for electrical power and for the electronic enthusiast this must be attractive because it is virtually an electronic system. Panels of solar cells are attached to the coachroof or other convenient horizontal surfaces on the yacht. At best each panel will produce about 1 amp so to compensate for the battery drain you need several. They will work with lower efficiency when it is overcast, but they will not work when it is dark, just when you need your electrical supply most. Perhaps the strongest argument against solar power is the cost of the panels but then you don't get anything for nothing.

The racing yachtsman is not going to accept any drag which slows him down yet he needs to keep his essential electronics going. Solar panels can help, but he will have to resort to running his engine, with the propeller disconnected of course, or take on board a portable internal combustion generator. Most yachtsmen would not tolerate the noise, but the dedicated racing man, for whom electronics are now essential to winning, will put up with the noise. A reliable electrical system of one form or another is a pre-requisite of a reliable electronic system. Electronics are going to change the pattern of yachting. Electrical power has now become an essential feature on board yachts.

Index

Accuracy 9, 107
Admiralty List of Radio Signals 46
Alarm systems 132-134
Antennae 19-20, 128, 139-141
Autopilots 55-69
   controls 69
   interfacing 67
   man-overboard 134
   microprocessor 69
   power 69
   tiller/wheel steering 69

Back-up systems 89, 110
   Loran/Decca 110
Beacons, RDF 45
Bilge alarms 133

C/A code 28
CB radio 115, 120, 139
Cellular radio 115-6
Charts 76-82
   accuracy 79
   correcting 80
   characteristics 79
   data base 81
   digitisers 80
   electronic 77
   integration 81
   interfacing 79
   overlays 79
   paper 77-8
   scale 79
Collision avoidance 99-105
Colour radar 41
Compasses 55-69
   fluxgate 65
Computers 83-5
   hand-held 84
   tidal calculations 85
Control keys 19
Course planning 108

Damp 7
Decca 9, 10, 21, 72
   errors 11
   integration 86
   range 11
   reliability 12
   superceded 31
   waypoint navigation 12
Deviation, RDF 49, 51
Differential systems 20
Doppler 22-23
Duplex 114

Echo-sounder 55-69
   accuracy 60
   beam 57
   calibration 60
   frequencies 56-7
   fouling 63
   operation 55
   performance 56
   power 57
   presentation 58
   pulse rate 58
   range 57

   recording types 60
   speaking 60
   video 60
Electrical systems 127-141
Electronic charts 77, 83
Electronic plotters 77
Engine monitoring 130
EPIRBS 122-125
European Space Agency 30
Fax 111
Fire detectors 132
Fluxgate compasses 65
french Lighthouse Authority 18
Fuel consumption 131
Fuel economiser 130
Future developments 21

Gas alarms 133
Geostar 31-2
Glonass 30
Granas 31
Great circle 26
Grounds 139, 140
Guard zones 39

Half convergency 50
HF 117, 128
   antennae 139
Hi Fi 129-30
Hyperbolic systems 9, 18, 93
   accuracy 21

INMARSAT 30, 124
IOR 111
Installation 135-141
   power boats 137-8
   sailing yachts 138
Integrated electronics 85-90, 136
   satnav 86
   Decca 86
   Loran 86
   Navstar 86
   Radar 87
   Omega 86
Interference 136-7

Landfall 95
Lat/long 93-4
Lead 55
Log 55-69
   accuracy 64
   adjustment 64
   Doppler 61, 63
   electromagnetic 63
   errors 64
   fouling 62
   impellers 61
   towed 61
   types 61
Loran C 9, 12-15, 18, 72
   accuracy 15
   antennae 19
   errors 14
   filters 15
   frequencies 14
   group repetition intervals 14
   interference 14

   integration 86
   superceded 31
   US coverage 21
Loran C/Satnav 86
Man overboard 133
Memory 137
Mercator 76
MF-SSB 116-7, 128
   antennae 139
Morse Code 126

National Marine Electronics Association 90
Navigation 91-105
   poor visibility 99-105
   radar 96
   waypoint 18, 94
Navstar GPS 21-30, 80, 110
   accuracy 29
   integration 86
Navtex 120-22, 126, 139
Night effect 49
NOVA 27
Null point 47
Omega 16
   accuracy 17
   antennae 19
   corrections 17
   frequencies 17
   integration 86
Omega/Satnav 96
OMNI 52

P-Code 28
Plotters 76
Plotting table 77
Polar diagrams 109
Poor visibility 104-5
Portable radio 119, 134
   CB 120
Position lines 91
   Loran/Decca 92
Power supplies 8, 135-141
Power yachts 136
Pressure switches 133

Racal-Decca 10
Racing 106-111
   computers 109
   efficiency 109
   Loran/Decca etc 109
   RDF 110
   VMG 109
   weather 106
Radar 33-44
   antennae 36, 40
   clutter 37
   compass input 40
   collision avoidance 99
   colour 41
   detectors 44
   future 43
   guard zones 39
   installation 40
   performance 35, 42
   problems 34
   PRF 34
   pulse 34

radial scan 37
ranges 39
raster scan 37
true motion 44
VRM 38, 42
Radio 113-129
Radio lighthouses 53
RANA 18
RDF 45-54
    antennae 47
    accuracy 51
    beacons 45
    calibration 48-9
    errors 46, 48-9
    null 47
    range 46-7
    receivers 50
    refraction 49
Receivers 18, 50
Redundancy 7
Refraction 49
Repeatability 20
Rhumb line 26

Safety 129-134
Sailing efficiency 106, 109
SARSAT-COSPAS 123-5
Satellites 22-32
    NOVA 27

Transit 27
Glonass 30
Navstar 27
weather 112, 125
Satellite communications 113, 117-9
SatNav 22-32
Search and rescue RDF 54
Security 109-134
Shaft generator 142
Simplex 114
Skywaves 13-15
Smoke alarms 132
Solar panels 142
Sonar 60
Sonic Speed 63
Soviet Union 30
SSB 50, 54, 116-7

Television 129
    antennae 130
Telex 119-121
Tidal calculations 85
Toran 9, 18, 21
Traditional skills 7
Transducers 55, 139-141
Transit 22-24
    accuracy 24-5
    control panel 26
    displays 26

with Loran/Omega 24
antennae 27
Twelve metres 73, 106

UHF 115
US Coastguard Lights List 46
US Defence Mapping Agency 14
US Government 30
US Navy 27

VHF 19, 113-6, 134, 136
    antennae 128, 139
    distress 114
    modes 114
VHF DF 52
Video echo sounder 60
Visibility 99-105
VMG 72-3, 109

Waypoint navigation 18, 94
Weatherfax 125-8
Weather forecasts 106, 111
Wind generators 141
Weatherproofing 139
Wind direction 70-5
Windspeed 70-5
Wind pressure 74-5